# New Psalms and Hymns and Spiritual Songs

*by*

## Carl P. Daw Jr.

CODE NO. 1755

**Hope Publishing Company**
CAROL STREAM IL 60188

©1996 by Hope Publishing Company
380 South Main Place, Carol Stream, IL 60188
International Copyright Secured. All Rights Reserved.
Printed in the United States of America

# TABLE OF CONTENTS

**New Spiritual Songs**

**Indexes**

# INTRODUCTION

At a conference several years ago I heard Donald Hustad suggest that the phrase "psalms and hymns and spiritual songs" found in two New Testament epistles (Ephesians 5.19 and Colossians 3.16) may be a kind of Trinitarian formula linking each genre of musical praise with a corresponding Person of the Trinity. In other words, "psalms" would be related to the First Person (traditionally called God the Father), "hymns" to the Second Person (traditionally, God the Son), and "spiritual songs" to the Third Person (God the Holy Spirit). He did not press the point but merely left this interpretation as an intriguing possibility.

In any case, the seed planted by his suggestion has ultimately borne fruit in the organization of this collection. Each of this book's three divisions develops a cluster of hymnody related to one of the Persons of the Trinity. Adopting such restrictions of form and content has proved a valuable way to approach the creation of texts as brief and intense as hymns need. On the other hand, there are some real limitations to this approach: for example, texts dealing with the full Trinity do not fit well into this three-part pattern. (They appear in the third section, because of the Holy Spirit's activity in maintaining the unity of the Godhead.) Yet the virtues of intensity and clarity have generally outweighed any inconveniences imposed by the choice of these ground rules.

Because I have learned through experience that people are more likely to attempt a new hymn if it is printed with music, the texts in this collection all appear with at least one tune. Several texts have two or three tunes printed with them; others carry suggestions for alternative tunes found elsewhere. I am grateful to all the composers who have given permission for their music to be included here, and especially to those who have created settings specifically for my texts. In a few instances, I have even ventured to set down the tunes I heard in certain texts.

At the end of this volume, brief notes provide some description of the scripture references and other influences in the shaping of these texts. They also give condensed information regarding the tunes printed here as well as advice on where to find the alternative tunes. The notes are followed by six indexes: scripture, topical, metrical, tune-name, composers, and first-line. To compensate for the lack of such aids in my earlier collections, these indexes are all cumulative and cover the three collections of my texts published thus far.

I am thankful for the various groups who commissioned texts included here; their myriad occasions contributed to the broadening and strengthening of this book. I have also appreciated the patience and encouragement of Hope Publishing Company, especially from its Chairman, George Shorney, and from Jack Schrader, the Executive Editor. The greatest supporter (and keenest critic) throughout this project has been, as always, my wife May, to and for whom I am grateful beyond telling.

Carl P. Daw, Jr.

# 1 As Newborn Stars Were Stirred to Song

*Unison*

1. As new-born
2. In psalms that
3. When God's re-
4. But si - lence

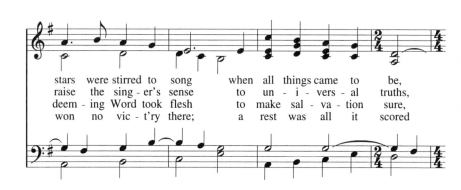

stars were stirred to song when all things came to be,
raise the sing-er's sense to un - i - vers - al truths,
deem - ing Word took flesh to make sal - va - tion sure,
won no vic - t'ry there; a rest was all it scored

as Mir - i - am and Mos - es sang when
in proph - et's dark - toned o - ra - cle or
un - heed - ing hearts at - tuned to strife re -
be - fore glad al - le - lu - ias rose to

WORDS: Carl P. Daw, Jr.
MUSIC: John Karl Hirten

ALEXANDRA
C.M.D.

# New Psalms

The texts in this division are of two main kinds: those that paraphrase or reflect on the content of canonical psalms and those that imitate the style of such scripture. Unlike Isaac Watts, I have not introduced anachronistic Christian interpretations but have tried to work with the psalms' own wealth of images for God. At the same time, I have tried to give some immediacy and familiarity to the recurring human circumstances and enduring emotions woven through these songs of longing, hope, and praise.

# 2  Beneath the Proud Hills' Shadows

1. Be - neath the proud hills' shad-ows I seek the help I need.
2. "Your foot will nev - er stum-ble, nor will your Guard-ian sleep;
3. "From ev - ery harm and e - vil your life will be se - cure;

I lift my eyes be - yond them and there this prom-ise read:
the One who cares for Is - rael will ev - er watch-ful keep.
God's strength and love will guard you and keep your foot-ing sure.

"Help comes from God Al - might-y, who made both heav'n and earth,
The Lord will be your shade tree to shield you day and night;
Your com-ings and your go - ings are all with - in God's hand;

the Lord who ban-ished cha - os and brought all things to birth.
the sun's heat can - not hurt you nor can the moon's pale light.
the Lord will bless and keep you till no more proud hills stand."

WORDS: Carl P. Daw, Jr.
MUSIC: *Southern Harmony*, 1835; harm. Hal H. Hopson

COMPLAINER
7.6.7.6.D.
Suggested Alternate Tune: LLANGLOFFAN

# 3 By the Waters of Babylon

*Three-Part Canon*

1. By the wa - ters, the wa - ters of Bab - y - lon,
2. On the wil - lows, the wil - lows of Bab - y - lon,
3. Those who car - ried us, who car - ried us to Bab - y - lon,
4. On the al - ien soil, the al - ien soil of Bab - y - lon,
5. By the wa - ters, the wa - ters of Bab - y - lon,

we sat down and wept, and wept for thee, Zi - on.
we hung up our harps, our harps brought from Zi - on.
asked us for a song, a song of thee, Zi - on.
how dare we to praise, to praise thy God, Zi - on?
we sat down and wept, and wept for thee, Zi - on.

We re - mem - ber thee, re - mem - ber thee, re - mem - ber thee, Zi - on.
We re - mem - ber thee, re - mem - ber thee, re - mem - ber thee, Zi - on.
We re - mem - ber thee, re - mem - ber thee, re - mem - ber thee, Zi - on.
We re - mem - ber thee, re - mem - ber thee, re - mem - ber thee, Zi - on.
We re - mem - ber thee, re - mem - ber thee, re - mem - ber thee, Zi - on.

WORDS: Stanzas 1, 5: Traditional, based on Psalm 137; stanzas 2–4: Carl P. Daw, Jr.
MUSIC: Traditional melody

BY THE WATERS
Irregular

*Stanzas 2–4 © 1996 Hope Publishing Company, Carol Stream, IL 60188. All rights reserved.*

# 4 For God Alone My Soul in Silence Waits

1. For God a - lone my soul in si - lence waits; my help comes
2. In si - lence wait, my soul, for God a - lone, from whom comes
3. Like fleet - ing breath our world - ly hon - ors wane, and mor - tal

WORDS: Carl P. Daw, Jr.
MUSIC: Melody and bass, Orlando Gibbons; harm. Ralph Vaughan Williams

SONG 1
10.10.10.10.10.10.

*Words © 1996 Hope Publishing Company, Carol Stream, IL 60188. All rights reserved.*
*Music from the **English Hymnal** by permission of Oxford University Press.*

from the Lord, my for - tress tower, my rock of strength that
hope through all life's change and chance. No oth - er rock, no
fame dis - solves like pass - ing dreams: light - er than air up -

keeps my foot - ing firm de - spite all those who would my
pow'r of height or depth, can keep you safe or bring de -
on an emp - ty scale is pride in wealth ac - quired by

life de - vour. Be not de - ceived: though with their lips they bless,
liv - er - ance. O peo - ple, put your trust in God al - ways;
cun - ning schemes. With God, en - dur - ing pow'r and love are one;

their hearts are filled with curs - ing wick - ed - ness.
pour out your hearts and give our Ref - uge praise.
then wait, my soul, for help from God a - lone.

# 5 From the Womb

1. From the womb, from the womb, you have known me, O Lord, from the womb. Before I thought or planned, my life was in your hand; you have known me, O Lord, from the womb.
2. Ev-ery-where, ev-ery-where, you pur-sue me, O Lord, ev-ery-where. Un-sleep-ing day and night, nor bound by depth or height, you pur-sue me, O Lord, ev-ery-where.
3. Still you call, still you call, though I wan-der, O Lord, still you call. When wild and proud I roam, your love in-vites me home; though I wan-der, O Lord, still you call.
4. In-to life, in-to life, you will lead me, O Lord, in-to life. Through death's dark shad-ow passed, to see your face at last, you will lead me, O Lord, in-to life.

WORDS: Carl P. Daw, Jr.
MUSIC: Carl P. Daw, Jr.; harm. David Ashley White

WARDSONG
6.9.6.6.9.

# 6 From the Womb

*Unison*

1. From the womb, from the womb, you have known me, O Lord, from the womb. Be-fore I thought or planned, my life was in your hand; you have known me, O Lord, from the womb.

2. Ev-ery-where, ev-ery-where, you pur-sue me, O Lord, ev-ery-where. Un-sleep-ing day and night, nor bound by depth or height, you pur-sue me, O Lord, ev-ery-where.

3. Still you call, still you call, though I wan-der, O Lord, still you call. When wild and proud I roam, your love in-vites me home; though I wan-der, O Lord, still you call.

4. In-to life, in-to life, you will lead me, O Lord, in-to life. Through death's dark shad-ow passed, to see your face at last, you will lead me, O Lord, in-to life.

WORDS: Carl P. Daw, Jr.
MUSIC: John Bell

IMMACULATA
6.9.6.6.9.

# 7 Give Us New Songs, O God

*Unison*

1. Give us new songs, O God, new words and tunes to tell the won-der of your love, till hearts and voic-es swell to join the an-gels' end-less song, to join the an-gels' end-less song, to join the an-gels'
2. Teach us new mel-o-dies; with new breath fill our lungs; with ring-ing words of truth a-rouse our si-lent tongues to join the an-gels' end-less song, to join the an-gels' end-less song, to join the an-gels'
3. Sing through our dai-ly rounds; u-nite our lives to make a liv-ing hymn of praise, un-til from death we wake to join the an-gels' end-less song, to join the an-gels' end-less song, to join the an-gels'

WORDS: Carl P. Daw, Jr.
MUSIC: Richard Wayne Dirksen

WYNGATE CANON
6.6.6.6.8.8.

*for canon only*

end - less song.
end - less song.
end - less song.

## 8 How Good, How Pleasant to Behold

*Unison*

1. How good, how pleas - ant to be - hold the joy of
2. Like sooth - ing oil that trick - les down a sun-parched
3. The last - ing peace be-stowed by God en - dures when

lives in har - mo - ny, not simp - ly peo - ple shar - ing
head, or sum - mer's dew that makes the hills of Zi - on
hu - man ef - forts fail, so bless - ing life to - geth - er

space but minds and hearts in true ac - cord.
glad: such is the balm of true sha - lom.
here that we may grasp e - ter - nal joy.

WORDS: Carl P. Daw, Jr.
MUSIC: Traditional English melody; harm. Martin West

O WALY WALY
L.M.
Suggested Alternate Tune: JACOB

# 9 How Sweet Was the Garden, Fertile and Fair

1. How sweet was the gar - den, fer - tile and fair,
2. We free - ly could eat from all but one tree
3. From dark, bit - ter fruit came forth a bright seed,

the first and best home God gave to our care,
(for - bid - den, per - haps, lest gods we might be?),
for God did not turn from us in our need:

a par - a - dise lav - ished on crea - tures of clay;
but tast - ing, we grew not di - vine af - ter all:
the Love that first formed us em - brac - es us still

yet we were not will - ing to fol - low God's way.
the fruit in our mouth turned from nec - tar to gall.
and woos us from wan - d'ring to fol - low God's will.

WORDS: Carl P. Daw, Jr.
MUSIC: *Whole Book of Psalmes*, 1621

OLD 104TH
10.10.11.11.

# 10 How Sweet Was the Garden, Fertile and Fair

*Unison*

1. How sweet was the gar - den, fer - tile and fair, the
2. We free - ly could eat from all but one tree (for -
3. From dark, bit - ter fruit came forth a bright seed, for

first and best home God gave to our care, a
bid - den, per - haps, lest gods we might be?), but
God did not turn from us in our need: the

par - a - dise lav - ished on crea - tures of clay; yet
tast - ing, we grew not di - vine af - ter all: the
Love that first formed us em - brac - es us still and

we were not will - ing to fol - low God's way.
fruit in our mouth turned from nec - tar to gall.
woos us from wan - d'ring to fol - low God's will.

WORDS: Carl P. Daw, Jr.
MUSIC: Rusty Edwards

LONG ISLAND SOUND
10.10.11.11.

# 11 Not for Ourselves, O Lord, Not for Ourselves

1. Not for our-selves, O Lord, not for our-selves
2. The world-ly say of us: "Where is their God?"
3. But we will trust in God, our help and shield,

would we claim glo - ry, but for you a - lone,
They vain - ly look for what they i - dol - ize,
tran - scend - ent Life on whom all lives de - pend,

be - cause of your great love and faith - ful - ness,
for flaunt - ed wealth, for burn - ished im - ag - es,
whose un - told mer - cies give our spir - its voice

the stead - fast care that makes your pres - ence known.
and trim all gods to their own shape and size.
to bless the Lord in songs that nev - er end.

WORDS: Carl P. Daw, Jr.
MUSIC: Orlando Gibbons

SONG 24
10.10.10.10.

# 12 O God Who Made Us in Your Likeness

*Unison*

1. O God who made us in your like-ness and gave the
2. To bear your im-age gives us free-dom to love, to
3. How did we lose our birth-right bless-ing? Why do we
4. We have mis-used our god-like free-dom, re-belled and
5. Where shall we turn when our ways fail us? We have no

world in-to our care that we might rule and serve cre-
rea-son, and to choose; yet we fall short of your in-
live a-part from God? What has un-webbed us from cre-
fol-lowed our own schemes; in place of God we have in-
help but God a-lone. Teach us, O God, your truth; re-

a-tion, we come be-fore you with this prayer:
ten-tion and our cre-a-tive pow'rs a-buse.
a-tion, so that we feel a-lone and odd?
vent-ed vain i-dols spun from fears and dreams.
claim us, till in our lives your will is known.

Re-store in us your im-age, O God.

WORDS: Carl P. Daw, Jr.
MUSIC: Alfred V. Fedak

IMAGO DEI CAZENOVIA
9.8.9.8.Ref.

# 13 O Sing to the Lord with Hymns Newly Made

*Three-Part Canon*

WORDS: Carl P. Daw, Jr.
MUSIC: Carl P. Daw, Jr.

LOOSE CANON
10.10.10.5.

# 14 Sing Praise to God, Whose Mighty Acts

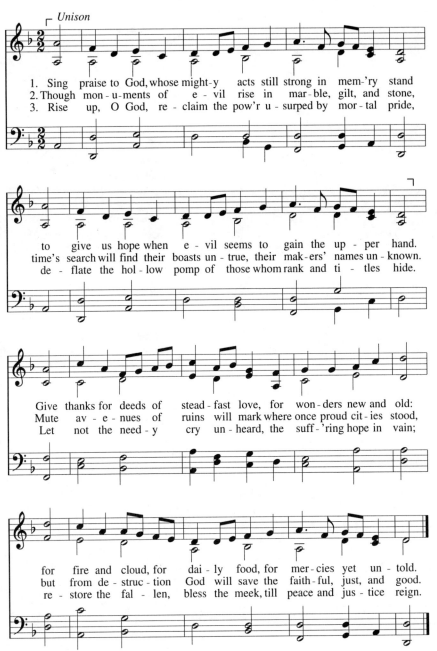

*Unison*

1. Sing praise to God, whose might-y acts still strong in mem'ry stand
2. Though mon-u-ments of e-vil rise in mar-ble, gilt, and stone,
3. Rise up, O God, re-claim the pow'r u-surped by mor-tal pride,

to give us hope when e-vil seems to gain the up-per hand.
time's search will find their boasts un-true, their mak-ers' names un-known.
de-flate the hol-low pomp of those whom rank and ti-tles hide.

Give thanks for deeds of stead-fast love, for won-ders new and old:
Mute av-e-nues of ruins will mark where once proud cit-ies stood,
Let not the need-y cry un-heard, the suff-'ring hope in vain;

for fire and cloud, for dai-ly food, for mer-cies yet un-told.
but from de-struc-tion God will save the faith-ful, just, and good.
re-store the fal-len, bless the meek, till peace and jus-tice reign.

WORDS: Carl P. Daw, Jr.
MUSIC: *Kentucky Harmony*, 1816; harm. *Songs for Liturgy & More Hymns & Spiritual Songs*, 1971

SALVATION
C.M.D.

# 15 Sing to the Lord No Threadbare Song

1. Sing to the Lord no thread-bare song, no time-worn, tooth-less hymn,
2. Let earth's di-verse, me-lo-dic tongues de-clare in tell-ing phrase
3. Heav-ens re-joice, and earth be glad! Ex-ult, you roar-ing seas!

no sen-ti-ment-al plat-i-tude, no emp-ty pi-ous whim; but
the glo-ry of the on-ly God who mer-its thanks and praise. All
Let fields and plains re-sound with joy that ech-oes from the trees! As

raise a song just off the loom, fresh-wov-en, strong, and dense, as
oth-er hopes will dis-ap-point, their brit-tle lus-ter fade, but
na-ture sings, let peo-ple join and hu-man dis-cord cease, for

new as God's e-ter-nal now tran-scend-ing time and sense.
sure and strong re-mains the Lord by whom all things were made.
God shall come to rule the world with jus-tice, love, and peace.

WORDS: Carl P. Daw, Jr.
MUSIC: Alfred V. Fedak

CANTICUM NOVUM
C.M.D.

# 16 When God First Brought Us Back from Exile

*Unison*

1. When God first brought us back from ex - ile, we were as
2. Once more, O Lord, re - store your peo - ple; come with your

dazed as those who dream. Then were our mouths brim - ming with
sav - ing help a - gain, as to the brook - beds in the

laugh - ter; joy from our lips gushed like a stream. The god - less
des - ert you bring the sweet, re - viv - ing rain. Let those who

cried in en - vious won - der, "Look what the Lord has done for them!" In - deed our
sow with tears and sigh - ing sing as they reap and joy pro - claim; may those who

God has great - ly blessed us; re - joice and sing, Je - ru - sa - lem!
weep when seed is scat - tered gath - er their sheaves and praise your Name.

WORDS: Carl P. Daw, Jr.
MUSIC: Traditional American melody; arr. Donald P. Hustad

WAYFARING STRANGER
9.8.9.8.D.

# New Hymns

The texts in this section focus on the life and ministry of Jesus Christ. As the notes at the back of this volume testify, these hymns are all intended to be connected with particular events in Jesus' life or specific aspects of his teaching. Their common thread is a concern to continue the mystery of the Incarnation into the present, into the lives of those who contemplate the revelation of God in Christ through the singing of these hymns. Contrary to the facile notion that "hymns" are objective and "songs" are subjective, the texts in this section implicitly argue that the greatest praise comes from lives that embody the self-giving love of God made known in Jesus Christ.

# 17 Baited, the Question Rose

1. Bait-ed, the ques-tion rose from some-where in the crowd:
2. "Whose im-age does it bear, whose name and ti-tles tell?"
3. May we dis-cern, O God, your dai-ly gifts of grace;

"Teach-er, you tru-ly know God's way; is pay-ing tax al-lowed?"
"Cae-sar's, of course," they smug-ly said and thought they an-swered well.
show us your im-age fresh-ly coined in ev-ery heart and face.

Je-sus per-ceived their trap: "Why do you test me so? Bring
"Give Cae-sar what is his; God, what is God's a-lone." Strong
Help us fit trib-ute yield through prayers and hymns we raise, but

here the coin the tax re-quires, and see what it will show."
words, con-vinc-ing and pro-found, like truth al-read-y known.
most of all by deeds of love to give you thanks and praise.

WORDS: Carl P. Daw, Jr.
MUSIC: Malcolm Williamson

MERCER STREET
S.M.D.

# 18 Bright the Cloud and Bright the Glory

**Spaciously** (♩ = c. 60) *Unison or parts*

1. Bright the cloud and bright the glo - ry (bright - er far than
2. Bright the cloud but dark the glo - ry wrought by hu - man
3. From the cloud and from the glo - ry hu - man need brought

mere sun's rays) o - pen - ing the gates of heav - en
en - ter - prise, o - pen - ing with aw - ful ter - ror
Je - sus down: down to death, then from death ris - ing

to dis - ci - ples' awe - struck gaze: pow - er past their
stark new worlds be - fore our eyes: pow - er grasped but
to re - ceive a vic - tor's crown. Lead us, Christ, to

sens - es' sav - ing, splen - dor too pro - found for praise. All was changed,
far from mas - tered, know - ledge keen but not yet wise. All has changed,
prize com - pas - sion more than might, wealth, or re - nown. Help us change,

WORDS: Carl P. Daw, Jr.
MUSIC: David Ashley White

HOLY TRINITY, THE AMERICAN CATHEDRAL
8.7.8.7.8.7.Ref.

all   was changed; and   they would   nev  -  er   be   the   same.
all   has changed; and   we    shall   nev  -  er   be   the   same.
help  us  change, that   we     may    nev  -  er   be   the   same.

# 19 Bright the Cloud and Bright the Glory

*Unison*

1. Bright the cloud and bright the glo - ry (bright - er far than
2. Bright the cloud but dark the glo - ry wrought by hu - man
3. From the cloud and from the glo - ry hu - man need brought

mere sun's rays) o - pen - ing the gates of heav - en
en - ter - prise, o - pen - ing with aw - ful ter - ror
Je - sus down: down to death, then from death ris - ing

to dis - ci - ples' awe - struck gaze: pow - er past their
stark new worlds be - fore our eyes: pow - er grasped but
to re - ceive a vic - tor's crown. Lead us, Christ, to

sens - es' sav - ing, splen - dor too pro -
far from mas - tered, know - ledge keen but
prize com - pas - sion more than might, wealth,

WORDS: Carl P. Daw, Jr.
MUSIC: Alfred V. Fedak

LUX TREMENDA
8.7.8.7.8.7.Ref.

found  for  praise.  All  was  changed,  all  was  changed;
not  yet  wise.  All  has  changed,  all  has  changed;
or  re - nown.  Help  us  change,  help  us  change,

and  they  would  nev - er  be  the  same.
and  we  shall  nev - er  be  the  same.
that  we  may  nev - er  be  the  same.

# 20 Bright the Cloud and Bright the Glory

1. Bright the cloud and bright the glory
2. Bright the cloud but dark the glory
3. From the cloud and from the glory

1. (bright - er far than mere sun's rays) o - pen-ing the
2. wrought by hu - man en - ter - prise, o - pen-ing with
3. hu - man need brought Je - sus down: down to death, then

1. gates of heav - en to dis - ci - ples' awe - struck gaze:
2. aw - ful ter - ror stark new worlds be - fore our eyes:
3. from death ris - ing to re - ceive a vic - tor's crown.

1. pow - er past their sens - es' sav - ing, splen - dor too pro -
2. pow - er grasped but far from mas - tered, know - ledge keen but
3. Lead us, Christ, to prize com - pas - sion more than might, wealth,

WORDS: Carl P. Daw, Jr.
MUSIC: William Bradley Roberts

HACKETT
8.7.8.7.8.7.Ref.

found   for   praise.   All   was   changed,   all   was   changed;   and
not   yet   wise.   All   has   changed,   all   has   changed;   and
or   re -  nown.   Help   us   change,   help   us   change,   that

they   would   nev -  er   be   the   same.
we   shall   nev -  er   be   the   same.
we   may   nev -  er   be   the   same.

# 21 Christ, Faithful Sower, Scattering the Good Seed

*Unison*

1. Christ, faith-ful Sow-er, scat-ter-ing the good seed,
2. Where ston-y ha-tred makes the heart's soil bar-ren,
3. Teach us dis-cern-ment as the quick-ened seeds sprout,
4. Gird us with pa-tience when no har-vest ri-pens,

God's word of prom-ise, full of truth and grace:
may we sow love that roots in hid-den earth;
when weeds and good plants have to-geth-er grown,
lest we de-spair and think our la-bors vain;

give us, your peo-ple, cour-age, strength, and wis-dom,
where thorns of doubt, de-spair, and dis-cord threat-en,
to tell temp-ta-tions from the worth they mim-ic,
though it seem slow, your word of life will pros-per:

that we may serve you in this time and place.
help us bring faith, new hope, and peace to birth.
to seek your pur-pose rath-er than our own.
seed-time at length will yield a-bund-ant grain.

WORDS: Carl P. Daw, Jr.
MUSIC: Frederick G. Russell

LOMBARD STREET
11.10.11.10.

# 22 Consider Well the Lilies

*Unison*

1. Con-sid - er well the lil - ies that gild the field like flame,
2. if God so clothes the flow - ers that dai - ly bloom and die,
3. No beau - ty of cre - a - tion, no won - der an - y - where,

with splen - dor more than Sol - o-mon's, for all his wealth and
how can we then so fool-ish - ly on our own strength re-
no rare e - vent or mir - a - cle can with this grace com-

fame: se - rene, un - toil - ing, bright, and
ly? For God who gives us life and
pare: to turn from self to seek God's

mute, they make the heart ex - claim:
breath will all our needs sup - ply.
will and trust God's bound - less care.

WORDS: Carl P. Daw, Jr.
MUSIC: Richard Proulx

ALDINE
7.6.8.6.8.6.
Suggested Alternate Tune: SPRING

# 23 Far From Cyrene and the Libyan Coastlands

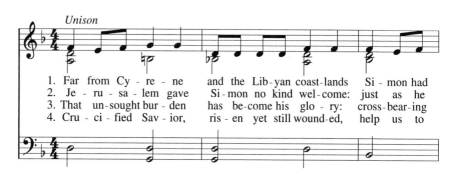

Unison

1. Far from Cy - re - ne and the Lib - yan coast-lands Si - mon had
2. Je - ru - sa - lem gave Si - mon no kind wel - come: just as he
3. That un-sought bur - den has be-come his glo - ry: cross-bear - ing
4. Cru - ci - fied Sav - ior, ris - en yet still wound-ed, help us to

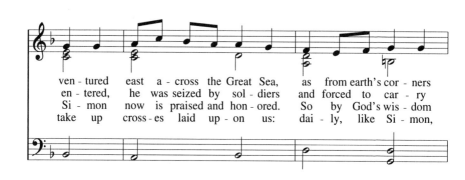

ven - tured east a - cross the Great Sea, as from earth's cor - ners
en - tered, he was seized by sol - diers and forced to car - ry
Si - mon now is praised and hon - ored. So by God's wis - dom
take up cross - es laid up - on us: dai - ly, like Si - mon,

faith and du - ty sum-moned Pass - o - ver pil - grims.
to the dread-ed Skull Place some friend-less Jew's cross.
much we find un - wel - come may prove a bless - ing.
shar-ing in your pas - sion, birth pangs of new life.

WORDS: Carl P. Daw, Jr.
MUSIC: Hank Beebe

BICKFORD
11.11.11.5.

# 24 Mixed Like Weeds in Wheatfields

*Unison*

1. Mixed like weeds in wheat-fields, what fears and greed we learn
2. Then a wan-d'ring teach-er ar-rives from Gal-i-lee
3. World-ly pow'r, un-daunt-ed, con-tin-ues to ap-plaud
4. Faith that roots in seed-time, en-dures the doubts of growth,

min-gled with the wis-dom of pru-dence and con-cern:
sow-ing words that pierce us yet some-how set us free:
self-ish-ness, op-pres-sion, re-venge, in-jus-tice, fraud.
blos-soms when en-cour-aged, bears pain and plea-sure both:

"Hoard the bet-ter vin-tage and serve a cheap-er wine";
"Be not cruel or venge-ful, but turn the oth-er cheek";
Though such e-vils flour-ish and grounds for hope de-crease,
find in us, great Sow-er, a fruit-ful plant-ing-place,

"Pearls that go un-hid-den get tram-pled by the swine."
"God will bless the hum-ble, the mer-ci-ful, the meek."
deep and well are plant-ed God's seeds of love and peace.
yield-ing in time's full-ness the har-vest of your grace.

WORDS: Carl P. Daw, Jr.
MUSIC: Carl P. Daw, Jr.

DARNEL
6.6.6.6.D

*Words and Music © 1996 Hope Publishing Company, Carol Stream, IL 60188. All rights reserved.*

# 25 Take Us as We Are, O God

1. Take us as we are, O God, and claim us as your own. As
once you chose to tell your love in hu-man flesh and bone, so
let our lives be used to make your sav-ing pur-pose known.

2. Bless us for your ser-vice, Lord; no pow-er we de-vise will
ev-er give us strength e-nough or make us tru-ly wise, yet
by your prom-ise we can know the peace your grace sup-plies.

3. Break us o-pen to dis-close how bro-ken-ness can heal, where-
ev-er bro-ken loaves suf-fice to give a crowd a meal and
graves break o-pen to re-lease new life from death's dread seal.

4. Give us to the world you love as light and salt and yeast, that
we may nour-ish in your name the last, the lost, the least, un-
til at length you call us all to your un-end-ing feast.

WORDS: Carl P. Daw, Jr.
MUSIC: Alfred V. Fedak

ENDLESS FEAST
7.6.8.6.8.6.

# 26 Travelers' Child Laid in a Manger

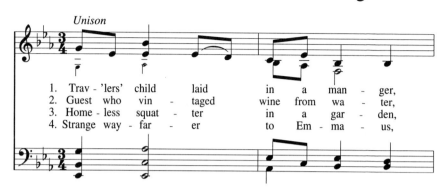

*Unison*

1. Trav - 'lers' child laid in a man - ger,
2. Guest who vin - taged wine from wa - ter,
3. Home - less squat - ter in a gar - den,
4. Strange way - far - er to Em - ma - us,

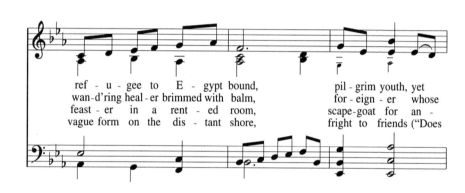

ref - u - gee to E - gypt bound, pil - grim youth, yet
wan - d'ring heal - er brimmed with balm, for - eign - er whose
feast - er in a rent - ed room, scape - goat for an -
vague form on the dis - tant shore, fright to friends ("Does

not a stran - ger when your Fa - ther's house you
hear - er brought her heart - thirst to your well of
oth - er's par - don, sleep - er in a bor - rowed
sense be - tray us?") when you stood with them once

WORDS: Carl P. Daw, Jr.
MUSIC: William Bradley Roberts

MISSISSIPPI
8.7.8.7.D.

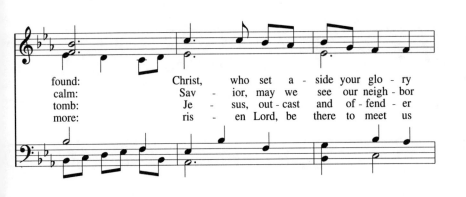

found:          Christ,    who set a - side your glo - ry
calm:           Sav - ior, may we    see our neigh - bor
tomb:          Je - sus, out - cast and of - fend - er
more:         ris - en Lord, be there to meet us

to re - claim our way-ward race,      help   us read sal -
as an em - blem of your care;      in   our lei - sure
to those cer - tain of God's will,     rend   the veils of
when life dawns e - ter - nal - ly;    may   your prom-ised

va - tion's sto - ry    in each pass - ing heart and face.
and our la - bor    give us grace to find you there.
race and gen - der, wealth and health, that shroud us still.
bless - ing greet us,   "In all these you wel - comed me."

# 27 Travelers' Child Laid in a Manger

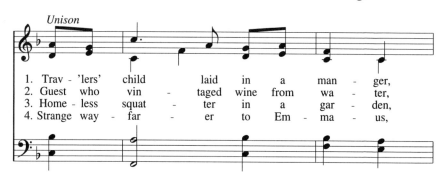

*Unison*

1. Trav - 'lers' child laid in a man - ger,
2. Guest who vin - taged wine from wa - ter,
3. Home - less squat - ter in a gar - den,
4. Strange way - far - er to Em - ma - us,

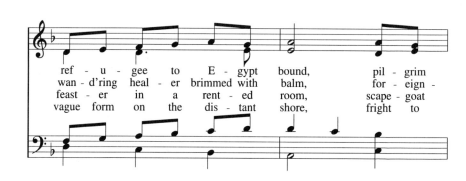

ref - u - gee to E - gypt bound, pil - grim
wan - d'ring heal - er brimmed with balm, for - eign -
feast - er in a rent - ed room, scape - goat
vague form on the dis - tant shore, fright to

youth, yet not a strang - er when your Fa - ther's house you
er whose hear - er brought her heart - thirst to your well of
for an - oth - er's par - don, sleep - er in a bor - rowed
friends ("Does sense be - tray us?") when you stood with them once

WORDS: Carl P. Daw, Jr.
MUSIC: Betty Carr Pulkingham

REFUGEE
8.7.8.7.D.

found: Christ, who set a - side your glo - ry to re -
calm: Sav - ior, may we see our neigh - bor as an
tomb: Je - sus, out - cast and of - fend - er to those
more: ris - en Lord, be there to meet us when life

claim our way - ward race, help us read sal - va - tion's
em - blem of your care; in our lei - sure and our
cer - tain of God's will, rend the veils of race and
dawns e - ter - nal - ly; may your prom - ised bless - ing

sto - ry in each pass - ing heart and face.
la - bor give us grace to find you there.
gen - der, wealth and health, that shroud us still.
greet us, "In all these you wel - comed me."

# 28 We See in Jesus a Love Beyond Telling

1. We see in Je - sus a love be - yond tell - ing:
2. Born as a mor - tal and yoked to our sto - ry,
3. Love that makes ho - ly by risk - ing and spend - ing
4. Bathed in that life let us feast at God's ta - ble,
5. Then let us go forth to pray by our liv - ing

in - fin - ite maj - es - ty hum - bly be - came
suf - fer - ing Serv - ant whose thanks was a cross,
con - quers sin's bond - age and scat - ters death's night;
tell - ing Christ's vic - t'ry with bread and with wine,
that love and mer - cy may dai - ly in - crease.

per - fect - ly im - per - fect, God with us dwell - ing,
Christ turned de - feat to a fore - taste of glo - ry:
so has Christ won for us life with - out end - ing,
of - f'ring our wor - ship as best we are a - ble,
Chal - lenged and strength-ened by God's own self - giv - ing,

Word tak - ing flesh, sav - ing Life giv - en name.
new life was won by what seemed ut - ter loss.
prom - ised God's pres - ence in free - dom and light.
here where the hu - man en - coun - ters di - vine.
may we be peo - ple of joy, hope, and peace.

WORDS: Carl P. Daw, Jr.
MUSIC: *Antiphoner*, harm. John Bacchus Dykes

O QUANTA QUALIA
11.10.11.10.

## 29 Were Tadpoles to Fly or Fireflies to Sing

*Unison*

1. Were tad-poles to fly or fire-flies to sing, were
2. Though leaf-less it bears a sing-le ripe fruit, sur-
3. Though dy-ing the fruit and dead-ly the tree, with-
4. The tree casts a shad-ow cent-ur-ies long through
5. Cre-a-tion is filled with won-ders to tell, yet

toad-stools to dance or blue-bells to ring, such
mount-ed by thorns and pierced branch and root, whose
in them a-bides a deep mys-ter-y: while
suf-f'ring, de-spair, in-just-ice, and wrong, yet
noth-ing it boasts can ev-er ex-cel this

mar-vels of na-ture might daz-zle or please, but
pale, with-ered cas-ing with crim-son is pied where
bit-ter the press-ing, the vin-tage is sweet, and
earth-wombed and wait-ing, like dawn af-ter night, the
mar-vel un-fath-omed by pen or by breath, a

none could com-pare with the rar-est of trees.
knife-edge has left a fresh gash in the side.
loaves it has leav-ened re-vive those who eat.
full-ris-en fruit yields a har-vest of light.
life-giv-ing love that is strong-er than death.

WORDS: Carl P. Daw, Jr.
MUSIC: Carl P. Daw, Jr./harm. Kevin R. Hackett

ROODSONG
10.10.11.11.

# 30 When Doubt and Fear Impale Our Hopes

1. When doubt and fear im - pale our hopes or
2. Yet pierc - ing joy no less re - veals how
3. Such are the won - ders of the cross, where

pain in - vades each nerve and pore, we
frail our strength, how vast God's grace: we
sin - ful pur - pose brings forth good: strange

grasp a - new the price of love as
meet the wound - ed Ris - en One and
par - a - dox of life through death, of

we the Cru - ci - fied im - plore: Ky - ri -
there a trans - formed cross em - brace. Chri -
pow'r made known through ser - vant - hood. Ky - ri -

WORDS: Carl P. Daw, Jr.
MUSIC: James Woodman

MARVIL
L.M.Ref.

# 31 Who Is My Neighbor, Lord?

(Opt. hand claps)

1. "Who is my neigh-bor, Lord?" a law - yer asked of Je - sus.
2. The sto - ry Je - sus told was not what was ex - pect - ed.
3. How have we failed to find God's im - age in each oth - er?
4. Still teach us, Lord, how love em - brac - es those the rest shun;

Can we con - fine our care to those who like and please us?
Could mer - cy come through one whom right - eous folk re - ject - ed?
Have we pre-sumed to scorn a sis - ter or a broth - er?
en - large our hearts till we no long - er need to ques - tion:

Who are our neigh-bors, Lord? Who are our neigh - bors, Lord?
Who are our neigh-bors, Lord? Who are our neigh - bors, Lord?
Who are our neigh-bors, Lord? Who are our neigh - bors, Lord?
Who are our neigh-bors, Lord? Who are our neigh - bors, Lord?

WORDS: Carl P. Daw, Jr.
MUSIC: Betty Carr Pulkingham

DAVID EARLE
6.7.6.7.6.6.

# New Spiritual Songs

This is the largest and most varied section of this collection. In part, that fact results from the inclusion here of a number of texts invoking all three Persons of the Trinity. But there are other factors at work, too. Unlike the widespread but superficial understanding of "spiritual" matters as interior, individual, and private, these texts assume that the Holy Spirit is also at work in matters social, corporate, and public. As the old adage puts it, "A prophet is a mystic in action, and a mystic is a prophet at prayer."

# 32 As Six-Winged Seraphs Volleyed Praise

1. As six-wing'd ser-aphs vol-leyed praise a-cross the Tem-ple's
2. Still grant us through our wor-ship, Lord, such mo-ments, pierc-ing

vault-ed frame, I-sai-ah glimpsed God's sov-ereign pow'r; but
and sub-lime, when vis-ion, par-don, and re-solve com-

awe soon turned to fear and shame. An an-gel then with
bine to thwart the bounds of time. Ig-nite us with your

sear-ing coal burned off his guilt and set him free to
fire of love, un-mesh the snares of sin we weave, and

WORDS: Carl P. Daw, Jr.
MUSIC: Thomas Tallis

TALLIS' LAMENTATION
L.M.D.

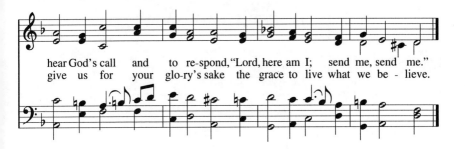

hear God's call and to re-spond, "Lord, here am I; send me, send me."
give us for your glo-ry's sake the grace to live what we be - lieve.

## 33 Beyond the Beauty and the Awe

*Unison*

1. Be - yond the beau - ty and the awe,
2. Our lives feel torn be - tween the world
3. Oh, teach us how to hear your voice
4. In sound or si - lence, sight or smell,
5. Then help us live as Je - sus taught,

be - yond the fear and dread, we long, O
whose needs are grim - ly real and emp - ty
de - spite the traf - fic's din, to keep the
may we some tok - en find that makes your
as light and salt and yeast, that oth - ers

God, to hear your word, to taste your trans-formed bread.
talk of peace and joy, with dis - tant, vague ap - peal.
blasts of ran - cor out and let your Spir - it in.
liv - ing pres - ence known to bod - y, soul, and mind.
may be brought to share your prom - ise and your feast.

WORDS: Carl P. Daw, Jr.
MUSIC: Patrick Michaels

ROFINOT
C.M.

# 34 Beyond the Beauty and the Awe

*Unison*

1. Be - yond the beau - ty and the awe, be -
2. Our lives feel torn be - tween the world whose
3. Oh, teach us how to hear your voice de -
4. In sound or si - lence, sight or smell, may
5. Then help us live as Je - sus taught, as

yond the fear and dread, we
needs are grim - ly real and
spite the traf - fic's din; to
we some tok - en find that
light and salt and yeast, that

long, O God, to hear your word, to
emp - ty talk of peace and joy with
keep the blasts of ran - cor out and
makes your liv - ing pres - ence known to
oth - ers may be brought to share your

**[1 - 4]**
taste your trans - formed bread.
dis - tant, vague ap - peal.
let your Spir - it in.
bod - y, soul, and mind.

**[5]**
prom - ise and your feast.

WORDS: Carl P. Daw, Jr.
MUSIC: Thomas Pavlechko

DOWNING
C.M.

# 35 Breath of God, Life-Bearing Wind

*Unison*

1. Breath of God, life - bear - ing wind, wak - ing
2. Breath of God, word - bear - ing wind, truth - re -
3. Breath of God, fire - bear - ing wind, source of
4. Breath of God, song - bear - ing wind, stir - ring

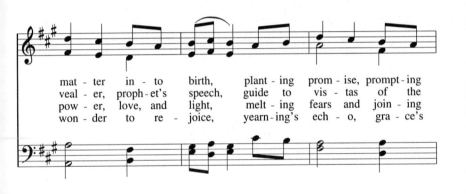

mat - ter in - to birth, plant - ing prom - ise, prompt - ing
veal - er, proph - et's speech, guide to vis - tas of the
pow - er, love, and light, melt - ing fears and join - ing
won - der to re - joice, yearn - ing's ech - o, gra - ce's

hope: with your life re - new the earth.
mind: let your word ex - cite and teach.
tongues: with your fire our hearts ig - nite.
dance: let your song give our prayers voice.

WORDS: Carl P. Daw, Jr.
MUSIC: Dorothy Howell Sheets

BINGHAM
7.7.7.7.

# 36 By Water and the Spirit

**Refrain**

*Unison or Harmony*

By wa-ter and the Spir-it bathed in glo-ry not our own, we are made a ho-ly peo-ple through whom God's love is shown.

*Unison*

1. O God who roused the light to birth and set the wa-ters'
2. O God of life who deigned to be of mor-tal moth-er
3. O God of bound-less en-er-gy, so wild in wind and
4. O God of three-fold life di-vine yet ev-er joined as

WORDS: Carl P. Daw, Jr.
MUSIC: Betty Carr Pulkingham

HOLY PEOPLE
C.M.D.Ref.

bounds, then lav-ished var - ied life on earth that still our
born, and shared the hos - pi - tal - i - ty of those whom
flame that those who sensed your mys - ter - y could nev - er
One, so may our words and deeds com-bine to let your

minds con - founds: re - vive your pow'r to form and bless, to
good folk scorn: re - move from us the names that blind by
be the same: stir up in us the will and strength to
will be done. Use ev - ery wo - man, man, and child to

con - quer gloom and strife, that where all seems bleak
gen - der, age, or race; your im - age may we
share your ur - gent might; trans - form us that our
min - is - ter your peace, till an - cient rifts be

*To Refrain*

emp - ti - ness, you yet may bring forth life.
seek and find in ev - ery heart and face.
lives at length may bear the Gos - pel's light.
rec - on - ciled, and proud di - vi - sions cease.

# 37 Dark and Comely, Evening Veils

(♩. = c. 68) Unison

1. Dark and come - ly, eve - ning veils all the
2. Speech - less night un - furls the stars hid - den
3. Might - y an - gels tend this night those who

glare and blare of day, slows down fran - tic
by the blaz - ing sun, stark re - buke when
work or watch or weep, and to all in

bus - y - ness, bids the faith - ful pause to pray:
hu - man pride thinks our world the on - ly one.
grief or pain bring the pre - cious balm of sleep.

"Glo - rious, thrill - ing gleam of God, Je - sus
Vast and dis - tant plan - ets dance far be -
Guard us night and day, O God; guide our

WORDS: Carl P. Daw, Jr.
MUSIC: Carlton R. Young

STOOKEY
7.6.7.6.7.7.7.6.
Suggested Alternate Tune: BORROWED LIGHT

Christ, blest ho - ly Light, bright - er far than
yond our prob - ing sense, tell - ing us how
dreams, our words, our deeds; give us grace to

ves - per lamps, fill and form our hymns to - night."
small we are, how un - earned God's prov - i - dence.
fill our lives with the Light this world still needs.

# 38 Faith Begins by Letting Go

Introduction/Interlude

1. Faith be - gins by let - ting go, giv - ing up what had seemed
2. Faith en - dures by hold - ing on, keep - ing mem - 'ry's roots a -
3. Faith ma - tures by reach-ing out, stretch-ing minds, en - larg - ing

sure, tak - ing risks and press - ing on, though the
live so that hope may bear its fruit; prom - ise
hearts, shar - ing strug - gles, liv - ing prayer, bind - ing

WORDS: Carl P. Daw, Jr.
MUSIC: David Hurd

JULION
7.7.7.7.7.7.

way    feels less se - cure:    pil - grim - age  both  right and
fed,    our souls will  thrive,    not through mer - it  we pos -
up     the bro - ken  parts:    till  we   find   the  com - mon -

odd,    trust - ing  all    our  life  to  God.
sess    but  by  God's    great faith - ful - ness.
place    ripe with  wit - ness  to  God's grace.

Coda

# 39 Friend of the Streetwalker, Beggar, and Child

*Unison*

1. Friend of the street-walk-er, beg-gar, and child,
lift-ing and bless-ing the weak and re-viled,
wel-com-ing those the de-vout turned a-way:
Je-sus, we need your ex-am-ple to-day.

2. Take from us prej-ud-ice, ha-tred, and scorn,
fear and sus-pi-cion of an-y-one born
out-side our fenc-es of mon-ey and race:
help us, O God, not to shun but em-brace.

3. O-pen our hearts and our heads and our hands,
let us ex-per-ience how car-ing ex-pands
past all the la-bels and lim-its we learn:
Spir-it of mer-cy, en-large our con-cern.

4. Three-per-soned Mys-ter-y, mul-ti-ple One,
joined by di-vers-i-ty nev-er un-done:
may we more tru-ly your im-age re-veal,
com-ing to-geth-er to make your love real.

WORDS: Carl P. Daw, Jr.
MUSIC: Alfred V. Fedak

MYRRH-BEARING MARY
10.10.10.10.

# 40 God Be with Us When We Gather Here

*Unison*

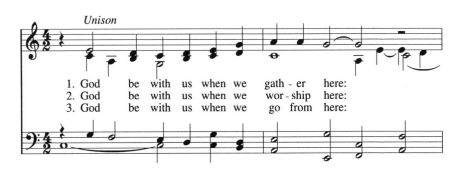

1. God be with us when we gath - er here:
2. God be with us when we wor - ship here:
3. God be with us when we go from here:

de - liv - er us from hard-ened hearts and wan-d'ring minds
be pres - ent in our midst to wak - en and com - bine
help us to bear your peace and love where there is strife,

when we as - sem - ble in your house of prayer.
your Spir - it's var - ied gifts so that we all
to find you in the least, the last, the lost.

WORDS: Carl P. Daw, Jr.
MUSIC: Alfred V. Fedak

EMMANUEL PARISH, WESTON
9.12.10.10.12.12.4.

# 41 God of Cosmos and of Atom

1. God of cos-mos and of a-tom, worlds great and small;
2. Spir - it weav-ing through cre - a - tion, plant, bird, and beast;
3. Christ, the Light who con - quers dark-ness, bring - ing re - lease;

Source of life too vast to fath-om, Mak - er of all:
all life's pow'r and in - spir - a - tion, great - est to least:
at whose cross, in ra - diant stark-ness, death's ter - rors cease:

when our boast-ing ends in blun-der, heal us with the joy of
with your grace re - store, re - make us; nev - er to our sins for -
fill us with your life un - end-ing; shield us by your con - stant

won - der, till through si - lence, song, or thun-der, we hear Love's call.
sake us; from en - tranc-ing er - ror wake us to taste Love's feast.
tend-ing, as we go forth by your send-ing to live Love's peace.

WORDS: Carl P. Daw, Jr.
MUSIC: Traditional Welsh melody

AR HYD Y NOS
8.4.8.4.8.8.8.4.

# 42 God of Wombing, God of Birth

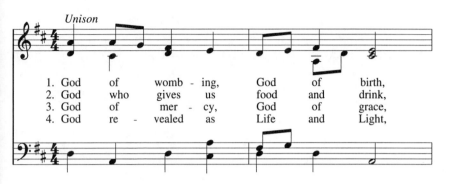

Unison

1. God of womb - ing, God of birth,
2. God who gives us food and drink,
3. God of mer - cy, God of grace,
4. God re - vealed as Life and Light,

God who formed us from the earth, wake your like - ness
hearts to love, and minds to think, day by day keep
swift to par - don and em - brace, from hate's lock - step
dawn of hope past death's dread night, through us prove your

in us still, quick - en us to do your will.
us a - ware all you give is ours to share.
set us free to re - pent, for - give, a - gree.
prom - ise true: you are mak - ing all things new.

WORDS: Carl P. Daw, Jr.
MUSIC: *Harmonia Sacra*

SAVANNAH
7.7.7.7.
Suggested Alternate Tune: THE CALL

# 43 Have We Any Gift Worth Giving

*Unison*

1. Have we an-y gift worth giv-ing to the Giv-er of all things?
2. Christ by cost-ly in-car-na-tion dwelt in hu-man time and place
3. Let us shun the self-ish mer-it world-ly wis-dom has de-fined,

What would please the ev-er-liv-ing one true God from whom life springs?
to re-veal to all cre-a-tion God's re-deem-ing love and grace:
but re-newed by God's own Spir-it be trans-formed in heart and mind:

Not dead gold or mer-chan-dise, but a liv-ing sac-ri-fice: wor-ship
so are we in flesh and bone giv-en means of mak-ing known through the
by past mer-cies taught and led, let us seek the path a-head, trust-ing

both pro-found and free-ing, serv-ing God with all our be-ing.
web of dai-ly liv-ing God's own pat-tern of self-giv-ing.
that, like those be-fore us, God will guide us and re-store us.

WORDS: Carl P. Daw, Jr.
MUSIC: Alfred V. Fedak

COSTLY GIFTS
8.7.8.7.7.7.8.8.

# 44 In Company with Every Age

1. In com - pa - ny with ev - ery age,
2. On Christ, the true foun - da - tion - stone,
3. Not on - ly for our needs we pray,
4. As Christ is known through Bread and Wine

we come to sing God's glo - ry,
our faith and hope are ground - ed;
but for the needs of oth - ers:
by grace be - yond our guess - ing,

as gath - ered in this ho - ly place,
we are up - held by God's own strength,
for friend and stran - ger, rich and poor,
so may our dai - ly lives be - come

we hear sal - va - tion's sto - ry.
the pow'r of love un - bound - ed.
new sis - ters, long - lost broth - ers.
the chan - nels of God's bless - ing.

WORDS: Carl P. Daw, Jr.
MUSIC: Irish melody

ST. COLUMBA
8.7.8.7.

# 45 Mighty God Who Called Creation

1. Might-y God who called cre-a-tion from the un-formed womb of space,
2. As we wor-ship, may your Spir-it breathe through us the pow'r of prayer,
3. Root-ed in the love of Je-sus, nour-ished by his flesh and blood,
4. Keep us faith-ful, joy-ful, lov-ing, filled with hope through grief and pain,

new-born worlds of gleam-ing glo-ry, fresh with hope and ripe with grace:
words of life for dai-ly liv-ing, strength to do and faith to dare.
may we prove a fruit-ful vine-yard joined in mu-tual ser-vant-hood.
know-ing that the One who made us has re-deemed and will sus-tain:

speak a-gain with pow'r and prom-ise when the storms of fear in-crease;
Come, en-flame us, Ho-ly Spir-it, like the Church at Pen-te-cost;
Work through us, O ris-en Sav-ior, to reap peace from fields of strife;
Tri-une God, of bound-less glo-ry, yet in hu-man form made known,

to our cha-os and con-fus-ion let your light and truth bring peace.
help us bear the light of bless-ing to the least, the last, the lost.
bring our bar-ren wastes to blos-som; lead us out of death to life.
raise us up to be a peo-ple called by love to be your own.

WORDS: Carl P. Daw, Jr.
MUSIC: C. Hubert H. Parry

RUSTINGTON
8.7.8.7.D.

# 46 Not Alone, but Two by Two

1. Not a-lone, but two by two, Je-sus sent dis-ci-ples out:
2. Have we still such dar-ing hearts? Can we claim their faith and nerve?
3. Ho-ly Spir-it, breathe through us with your u-ni-fy-ing might;

yoked to share their grow-ing faith, spurred by cour-age, slowed by doubt.
Do we tru-ly love the world Je-sus calls for us to serve?
kin-dle cleans-ing, melt-ing flames till our frac-tured wills u-nite.

Tak-ing but a walk-ing stick, mon-ey-less and san-dal-shod,
Can we plant a-gain the seed sown in mu-tual min-is-try,
Bind our hearts in mu-tual love, par-a-dox that sets self free;

forth they went to preach and heal, trust-ing all their needs to God.
pat-terned on a life of faith root-ed in com-mun-i-ty?
let our com-mon wit-ness show God's shared life in Trin-i-ty.

WORDS: Carl P. Daw, Jr.
MUSIC: Roy Hopp

TURNBERRY
7.7.7.7.D.
Suggested Alternate Tune: ABERYSTWYTH

# 47 O Boundless God, Who Chose to Bind

1. O bound-less God, who chose to bind your-self to us with
2. Blest Spir - it ev - er bind-ing God in mu - tual tri - une
3. O Christ whose be - ing binds in one a love both hu - man

stead-fast love, re - new in us your cov - e - nant that
u - ni - ty, stir us to em - u - late that bond in
and di - vine, trans - form our lives till they be - come like

we may still your peo - ple prove. Re - store those bless - ed
love for all hu - man - i - ty. Help us keep faith with
con - se - crat - ed bread and wine. Then as your Bod - y

char - ac - ters which a - pa - thy and sin have blurred; till
ag - es past, while tak - ing care for those un - born, and
use your Church to be a liv - ing tes - ta - ment, a

WORDS: Carl P. Daw, Jr.
MUSIC: L. Hoffer Simms

COVENANT
L.M.D.
Suggested Alternate Tune: CANDLER

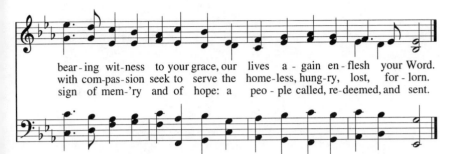

bear - ing wit - ness   to your grace, our   lives  a - gain en - flesh   your Word.
with com-pas - sion  seek to   serve the   home-less, hung-ry,   lost,   for - lorn.
sign  of mem-'ry  and of  hope: a   peo - ple called, re-deemed, and  sent.

# 48 O God in Whom All Life Begins

1. O God in whom all life be-gins, who births the seed to fruit,
2. U - nite in mu - tual min - is - try our minds and hands and hearts
3. Through tears and laugh-ter, grief and joy, en - large our trust and care;

be - stow your bless-ing on our lives; here let your love find root.
that we may have the grace to seek the pow'r your peace im - parts.
so bind us in com - mu - ni - ty that we may risk and dare.

Bring forth in us the Spir-it's gifts of pa - tience, joy, and peace;
So let our var - ied gifts com-bine to glo - ri - fy your Name
Be with us when we gath - er here to wor-ship, sing, and pray,

de - liv - er us from numb-ing fear, and grant our faith in - crease.
that in all things by word and deed we may your love pro - claim.
then send us forth in pow'r and faith to live the words we say.

WORDS: Carl P. Daw, Jr.
MUSIC: Roy Hopp

ACCORD
C.M.D.

# 49 O God in Whom All Life Begins

*Unison*

1. O God in whom all life be-gins, who births the seed to
2. U - nite in mu - tual min - is - try our minds and hands and
3. Through tears and laugh-ter, grief and joy, en - large our trust and

fruit, be - stow your bless-ing on our lives; here let your love find
hearts that we may have the grace to seek the pow'r your peace im-
care; so bind us in com - mu - ni - ty that we may risk and

root. Bring forth in us the Spir - it's gifts of pa - tience, joy, and
parts. So let our var - ied gifts com - bine to glo - ri - fy your
dare. Be with us when we gath - er here to wor - ship, sing, and

peace; de - liv - er us from numb-ing fear, and grant our faith in-crease.
Name that in all things by word and deed we may your love pro-claim.
pray, then send us forth in pow'r and faith to live the words we say.

WORDS: Carl P. Daw, Jr.
MUSIC: Kevin R. Hackett

RITTER
8.6.8.6.D.

# 50 O God Who Planted Eden Well

1. O God who plant-ed E - den well with trees both blest and cursed,
2. O Spir - it known in wind and flame, who kin - dled round a tree
3. O Christ, once hailed with boughs of palm, soon fad - ing to for - lorn
4. E - ter - nal Tri - une God of grace, bless us that we be made

yet would not thwart our hu - man will when daz - zled by the worst:
and from its un - burnt leaves breathed forth with pow'r un - named and free:
be - tray - al in an ol - ive grove and mock - ing crown of thorn:
like fruit - ful trees be - side a stream with leaves that nev - er fade:

from all the fu - tile, fruit - less sins we blame on age or youth,
as there you charged that Mo - ses stand on ho - ly ground un - shod,
help us to trust that seeds of hope root un - der weeds of strife,
es - tab - lish us with wis - dom's roots, our way - ward growth re - move,

en - tice our souls to taste and see the good - ness of your truth.
un - sheathe our guard - ed hearts and minds to feel and know our God.
as from the cross that wrought your death has sprung our tree of life.
and nour - ish us with faith and hope to bear the fruit of love.

WORDS: Carl P. Daw, Jr.
MUSIC: Traditional English melody; arr. Ralph Vaughan Williams

FOREST GREEN
C.M.D.

# 51 Praise God Who Gives All Blessings Birth

Praise God who gives all bless-ings birth; praise

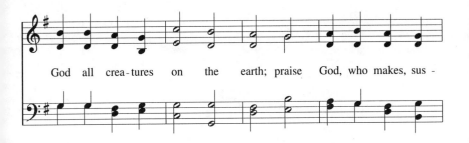

God all crea-tures on the earth; praise God, who makes, sus-

tains, sets free: one ho-ly God in Per-sons three.

WORDS: Carl P. Daw, Jr.
MUSIC: *Genevan Psalter*

OLD HUNDREDTH
L.M.
Suggested Alternate Tunes: TALLIS CANON,
LASST UNS ERFREUEN with Alleluias

# 52 Till All the Jails Are Empty

*Unison*

1. Till all the jails are emp-ty and all the bel-lies filled; till
2. In ten-e-ment and man-sion, in fac-tory, farm, and mill, in
3. By sit-ting at a bed-side to hold pale trem-bling hands, by

no one hurts or steals or lies, and no more blood is spilled; till
board-room and in bil-liard-hall, in wards where time stands still, in
speak-ing for the pow-er-less a - gainst un-just de-mands, by

age and race and gen-der no long-er sep-a-rate; till
class-room, church, and of-fice, in shops or on the street; in
pray-ing through our do-ing and sing-ing though we fear, by

pul-pit, press, and pol-i-tics are free of greed and hate:
ev-'ry place where peo-ple thrive or starve or hide or meet:
trust-ing that the seed we sow will bring God's har-vest near:

WORDS: Carl P. Daw, Jr.
MUSIC: John Bell

WORK TO DO
7.6.8.6.D.Ref.
Suggested Alternate Tune: ANTHEA

God       has  work  for  us  to  do.

# 53 We Come, O Christ, as People Seeking

*Unison*

1. We come, O Christ, as peo-ple seek-ing some sign of
2. To taste the cross with-in the chal-ice, to hear the
3. Re-new-ing Spir - it, come, breathe through us with hope that

bless-ing on our lives, yet scarce-ly pause to hear you
mu-sic born of grief, to feel the hurt con-cealed by
heals, with faith that thrills; burn off the sins still cling-ing

speak-ing or wait un - til your time ar - rives: help us let
mal-ice, to sense in doubt un-ripe be - lief: give us, O
to us, trans-form our minds, con-vert our wills: so may your

go, help us be still, in pa-tience may we learn your will.
God, new hearts, new eyes; wake us to love and make us wise.
gifts of grace in-crease to send us forth in love and peace.

WORDS: Carl P. Daw, Jr.
MUSIC: Alfred V. Fedak

RATHERVUE
9.8.9.8.8.8.
Suggested Alternate Tune: WER NUR DIE LIEBEN GOTT

# 54 We Sing for All the Unsung Saints

1. We sing for all the un-sung saints, that count-less, name-less throng,
2. Though un-in-scribed with date or place, with ti-tle, rank, or name,
3. So we take heart from un-known saints be-reft of earth-ly fame,

who kept the faith and passed it on with hope stead-fast and strong
as liv-ing stones their sto-ries join to form a hal-lowed frame
those faith-ful ones who have re-ceived a more en-dur-ing name:

through all the dai-ly griefs and joys no chron-ic-les re-cord,
a-round the mys-t'ry in their midst: the Lamb once sac-ri-ficed,
for they re-veal true bless-ing comes when we our pride ef-face

for-get-ful of their lack of fame, but mind-ful of their Lord.
the Love that wrest-ed life from death, the wound-ed, ris-en Christ.
and of-fer back our lives to be the ves-sels of God's grace.

WORDS: Carl P. Daw, Jr.
MUSIC: Traditional English melody; arr. Ralph Vaughan Williams

KINGSFOLD
C.M.D.

# 55 What Have You Here to Eat?

1. "What have you here to eat?" in - quired the ris - en Lord,
2. For here we feed up - on two mys - ter - ies di - vine:
3. "What have you here to eat?" still cries a world in need,
4. Come, take, bless, break, and give, with each at - tempt we make

and dazed dis - ci - ples found some fish a - mong their mea - ger hoard.
the ban - quet of God's ho - ly word and that of bread and wine.
through count - less hun - gry hearts and mouths that Christ gives us to feed.
to quench the hun - ger of the heart, to ease the bel - ly's ache:

"What have we here to eat?" a puz - zled Church ech - oes,
Trans - form - ing word and deed, these means of grace in - crease
Our loaves and fish - es fail, and weak our la - bors prove
that through us, ris - en Lord, all peo - ple may be fed,

for - get - ting what an end - less feast our life in Christ be - stows.
to nour - ish bod - y, soul, and mind and send us forth in peace.
un - til the Spir - it wakes in us the leav - en of God's love.
not on - ly with the food that fades but with your liv - ing Bread.

WORDS: Carl P. Daw, Jr.
MUSIC: Joseph Parry

DINBYCH
S.M.D.

# 56 When Everything Seems Possible

*Unison*

1. When ev-ery-thing seems pos-si-ble but cer-tain-ties are
yond the quest for pow'r and wealth (with fame's ad-dic-tive
noth-ing seems to sat-is-fy our nev-er-end-ing

few, when lim-its seem to dis-ap-pear and
buzz), be-yond each new tech-nol-o-gy that
greed, when count-less hu-man schemes have failed to

old rules yield to new, we
daz-zles as it does, we
fill our deep-est need, we

learn with pain-ful fre-quen-cy how
yearn for some-thing deep and true, for
turn to glimpse be-yond our-selves what

WORDS: Carl P. Daw, Jr.
MUSIC: William Bradley Roberts

CASADAY
C.M.D.
Suggested Alternate Tune: THE THIRD TUNE

small        our scope has        been,                    how
pur  -  pose, mean - ing,        worth:                    some
we        both need  and        lack:                        a

vast        and webbed the        half - grasped truths                    that
cos  -  mic clue  con  -  nect - ed        with                    our
God        who wait - ed,        loved, and        watched        un -

lie   be - yond our        ken.
be  -  ing  on  this        earth.
til        we should come

2.  Be -
3. When
back.

# 57 When We Feel Defeated

1. When we feel de-feat-ed, snared in doubt and wor-ry,
2. Though our hearts are ach-ing for some sign of bless-ing,
3. Great-er than our hop-ing, deep-er than our yearn-ing

no re-lief in sight; du-ties un-com-plet-ed, blun-ders galled by
we dis-guise our pain; masks of our own mak-ing keep us from ex-
for a sense of worth, light be-yond our grop-ing, goal of our re-

hur-ry, noth-ing work-ing right: shield us, Christ, from vain - de-spair;
press-ing what we long to gain: free-ing Spir-it, help us find
turn-ing, source of our re-birth: God of bound-less pow'r and love,

still the tem-pest, foil the Temp-ter when we feel de-feat - ed.
voice for faith's im-ag-in-a - tion though our hearts are ach - ing.
make in us a new cre-a - tion great-er than our hop - ing.

WORDS: Carl P. Daw, Jr.
MUSIC: Johann Crüger

JESU, MEINE FREUDE
6.6.5.6.6.5.7.8.6.

# Notes

# NOTES ON THE HYMNS

## 1. AS NEWBORN STARS WERE STIRRED TO SONG
This text on the centrality of music in the life of faith was commissioned by the San Francisco chapter of the American Guild of Organists to serve as the basis of a 1995 competition for new hymn tunes.

1. Biblical references in this stanza include Job 38.7 and Exodus 15.1-21.

2. Line 4 refers to the song attributed to Shadrach, Meschach, and Abednego during their ordeal in the fiery furnace. It appears in the book of the Apocrypha called The Prayer of Azariah and the Song of the Three Jews [or Three Young Men] and in Catholic Bibles following Daniel 3.23. The canticles *Benedicite, omnia opera Domini* and *Benedictus es, Domine* are drawn from this material; for metrical versions of them, see *To Sing God's Praise*, nos. 13-14 and 9-10.

3. Specific scriptural allusions in this stanza include John 1.14, Matthew 26.30/Mark 14.26, Matthew 27.46/Mark 15.34, and Psalm 22.

4. "Alleluia" is probably the most evocative and resonant word in the vocabulary of worship. It reaches English through Greek and Latin transliterations of a Hebrew phrase meaning "Praise the Lord." Because it is suppressed in Western liturgies during Lent, its reappearance at Easter intensifies its joyful connotations. Line 6 echoes 1 Corinthians 15.54-56.

*Tune*: ALEXANDRA, the winning tune in the San Francisco AGO competition, is named for the wife of the composer.

## 2. BENEATH THE PROUD HILLS' SHADOWS
This hymn paraphrases Psalm 121.

1. The hills circling Jerusalem are both physically and symbolically intimidating. Not only is the terrain challenging for travellers approaching or returning from the Temple; the greater height of the surrounding peaks also implies the spiritual superiority of the various local gods worshipped on each of them. Yet the God of Israel, who needs no such status symbol, is greater than them all.

*Tune*: COMPLAINER takes its name from the opening line of the text with which it appears in *Southern Harmony*: "I am a great complainer, that bears the name of Christ." The alternative Welsh tune LLANGLOFFAN is available in many hymnals.

### 3. BY THE WATERS OF BABYLON

This text is a paraphrase of Psalm 137.1-6.

*Tune*: Like most traditional melodies, BY THE WATERS survives in several forms and may be of Jewish origin. Its repetitive, stepwise patterns both suggest and contrast the downward flowing of water in Babylon and the laborious ascent of the hill of Zion, the two opposed experiences being bridged by the pathos of remembering.

### 4. FOR GOD ALONE MY SOUL IN SILENCE WAITS

This hymn paraphrases Psalm 62.

*Tune*: As its name recalls, SONG 1 was composed as a setting for the first song in George Wither's *Hymnes and Songs of the Church* (London, 1623). The text was a paraphrase of the Song of Moses from Exodus 15. Wither's stanza consisted of eight ten-syllable lines, with lines 5-6 of Gibbons' setting being repeated to accommodate the additional couplet.

### 5-6. FROM THE WOMB

This hymn does not paraphrase any particular psalm entirely. Instead, it collects ideas found in a variety of psalms and forms them into a new pattern, like a quilt formed from varied colors of cloth.

1. The imagery of this stanza echoes Psalm 22.9-10, Psalm 71.6, and Psalm 139.13-16. See also Isaiah 49.1 and Jeremiah 1.5.

2. This stanza compresses the imagery of Psalm 139.1-12 and includes an echo of Psalm 121.3-4.

3. This stanza blends ideas found in Psalm 27.8 (especially in the translation of the Book of Common Prayer, where it is verse 11 of the psalm) and Psalm 119.176.

4. Verses represented in this stanza include Psalm 34.22, Psalm 49.15, Psalm 23.4, Psalm 11.7, Psalm 17.15, and Psalm 27.8.

*Tune*: WARDSONG is much influenced by the shape-note tradition of American hymnody; in particular, measure 8 (including its pickup note) is a quotation from the tune WONDROUS LOVE. IMMACULATA is named for the parish church on the campus of the University of San Diego, where the composer and the author were among the presenters at the 1995 annual conference of the Hymn Society in the United States and Canada.

### 7. GIVE US NEW SONGS, O GOD

This text is a petitionary response to Psalm 98.1.

*Tune*: This text was written specifically for WYNGATE CANON in order to give this fine tune a text with wider applicability than William Walsham How's "You are the Christ, O Lord," for which it was composed. The tune name derives from the street on which the composer's eldest son's family lives.

## 8. HOW GOOD, HOW PLEASANT TO BEHOLD
This paraphrase of Psalm 133 could be appropriately used as a wedding hymn, at the blessing of a home, or for ecumenical or interfaith services.

*Tune*: O WALY WALY is an English folk melody collected and named by Cecil Sharp in his *Folk Songs from Somerset* (series 3, 1906). The attractive alternative tune JACOB by Jane Marshall appears in most recent hymnals.

## 9-10. HOW SWEET WAS THE GARDEN, FERTILE AND FAIR
Although the psalm of lament is a recognized genre, none of those collected in the Book of Psalms deals with the loss of Eden. This text explores some of the themes appropriate to a lament on this subject.

1. Genesis 2.8-15 (cf. 1.26-30).

2. Genesis 2.16-17; 3.1-19.

3. God's judgment is always tempered with mercy. Even the discovery of humanity's sin is accompanied by God's provision of clothing for these fallen and unprotected creatures (Genesis 3.21). Through succeeding generations God continued to call first individuals and then a nation to follow God's way.

*Tunes*: The selection of OLD 104TH actually preceded the writing of the text; it offered a blend of grandeur and pathos befitting the subject. LONG ISLAND SOUND was composed near that body of water to provide a setting for a twentieth-century lament for the fallen world, Fred Kaan's "We utter our cry."

## 11. NOT FOR OURSELVES, O LORD, NOT FOR OURSELVES
This hymn paraphrases Psalm 115.

*Tune*: Like SONG 1 at no. 4, SONG 24 provided a setting for the correspondingly numbered song in George Wither's *Hymnes and Songs of the Church* (London, 1623). In this instance the text was a paraphrase of the first chapter of Lamentations. Because Wither's stanzas contained six pentameter lines (a quatrain followed by a couplet), the second half of the tune was repeated to provide music for last two lines.

## 12. O GOD WHO MADE US IN YOUR LIKENESS
This hymn is modeled on the category of psalms known as "prayer songs of the community." Its use of a refrain has a precedent in a well-known example of such psalmody, Psalm 80, where the refrain is "Restore us, O God of hosts; show the light of your countenance, and we shall be saved"

(Book of Common Prayer translation). This text was commissioned for the sesquicentennial of the founding of St. Peter's Episcopal Church, Cazenovia, New York, and was premiered precisely on that anniversary on November 4, 1994. As the commissioners requested, the five stanzas deal with the topics discussed in the first section of the Outline of the Faith in the 1979 Book of Common Prayer (p. 845).

*Tune*: IMAGO DEI CAZENOVIA was commissioned for the occasion noted above and serves the text well, especially by directing energy and emphasis to the refrain.

### 13. O SING TO THE LORD WITH SONGS NEWLY MADE
This text is based on Psalm 149.

*Tune*: LOOSE CANON can be sung either in unison or as a canon. Hand-bells, either rung in clusters or playing the melody, would provide effective accompaniment.

### 14. SING PRAISE TO GOD, WHOSE MIGHTY ACTS
Psalm 9 provides much of the imagery and phrasing for this affirmation of the ultimate triumph of God's justice, despite the atrocities and boasts of those who flaunt worldly power.

*Tune*: The American folk melody SALVATION was published in the first Southern shape-note tune book, Ananias Davisson's *Kentucky Harmony* (Harrisonburg, VA, 1816). The tune is credited to Robert Boyd, a captain in the militia of Blount County, Tennessee. This harmonization is by Kenneth Munson, and first appeared in *Hymns for the Celebration of Life* (Boston, 1964).

### 15. SING TO THE LORD NO THREADBARE SONG
This hymn offers a fresh look at Psalm 96.

*Tune*: As its name implies and the text requires, CANTICUM NOVUM is indeed a new song, written especially for this collection. Its lilting triple rhythms invite dancelike, vigorous singing.

### 16. WHEN GOD FIRST BROUGHT US BACK FROM EXILE
This text paraphrases Psalm 126.

*Tune*: Concerning the formation of WAYFARING STRANGER, the arranger has noted: "The first part of the melody appeared in the Georgia *Sacred Harp* (1844). The last section is quoted in Nathanael Dett's *Folk Songs of the Negroes, sung at Hampton Institute* (1827). In both instances, the music is set to words other than the familiar folk text, 'I'm just a poor wayfaring stranger'" (*Companion to The Worshiping Church* [Carol Stream, IL, 1993], p. 21).

## 17. BAITED, THE QUESTION ROSE

The incident recalled in this hymn is told in all three synoptic gospels: Matthew 22.15-22/Mark 12.13-17/Luke 20.20-26.

*Tune*: MERCER STREET was composed as a setting for "This is my Father's world" in the second edition of *More Hymns and Spiritual Songs* (New York, 1977), at the request of its editor, Lee Hastings Bristol, whose home in Princeton, New Jersey, was on the street commemorated in the tune name. This tune should be sung slowly and reflectively (quarter note = 72).

## 18-19-20. BRIGHT THE CLOUD AND BRIGHT THE GLORY

This hymn was commissioned for the closing service of the 1995 Mississippi Conference on Church Music and Liturgy. That service fell on August 6, which was both the Feast of the Transfiguration and the fiftieth anniversary of the bombing of Hiroshima. It was requested that the hymn deal with this double significance of the day.

1. All three synoptic accounts (Matthew 17.1-13/Mark 9.2-8/Luke 9.28-36) mention a cloud; only Matthew calls it a "bright cloud."

3. The three synoptic accounts similarly agree in the sequence of events following the Transfiguration: after Jesus heals an epileptic boy, he once again tells his disciples of his coming passion (Matthew 17.14-23/Mark 9.14-32/Luke 9.37-45).

*Tunes*: Because of the unique occasion for which this text was written, it was shared with friends and at conferences in order to encourage as wide use as possible. As a result, a number of settings were produced, especially at the 1995 Hymnwriting Conference at St. Olaf College sponsored by the Hymn Society in the United States and Canada. HOLY TRINITY, THE AMERICAN CATHEDRAL was the tune commissioned by the Mississippi Conference and used there on August 6. Because it was written during the composer's springtime visit to Paris, it is named for the cathedral there with ties to the Episcopal Church in the United States. LUX TREMENDA was used on the same day at Westminster Presbyterian Church in Albany, New York, where its composer is Director of Music. HACKETT is named for Kevin Hackett (composer of the tune at no. 49 and harmonizer of no. 29), then a seminarian doing fieldwork at St. Philip's in the Hills Episcopal Church, Tucson, Arizona, whose Director of Music wrote this tune.

## 21. CHRIST, FAITHFUL SOWER, SCATTERING THE GOOD SEED

The parable of the sower and its interpretation appear in all three synoptic gospels (Matthew 13.3-9,18-23/Mark 4.2-9,13-20/Luke 8.4-8,11-15).

3. The parable of the wheat and tares appears only in Matthew 13.24-43. See also no. 24 in this collection.

4. Galatians 6.9; Isaiah 55.10-11.

*Tune*: LOMBARD STREET was composed as a setting for G.A. Studdert Kennedy's Industrial Christian Fellowship text "When through the whirl of wheels and engines humming." The tune name commemorates the location of the London church of St. Edmund King and Martyr, where the composer was organist for thirty years.

## 22. CONSIDER WELL THE LILIES
This well-known imagery from Jesus' teaching is recorded in Matthew 6.25-34 and Luke 12.22-31.

*Tune*: This text was written for the tune ALDINE, which is named for the Chicago street where the composer lives. His tune was composed for another pastoral text, Timothy Dudley-Smith's paraphrase of Psalm 19, "The stars declare his glory"; yet a subtly urban tone informs the accompaniment, especially in the Gershwinesque final cadence. The alternative tune SPRING by John Wilson can be found with this text in Hope Publishing Company's *Supplement 96*.

## 23. FAR FROM CYRENE AND THE LIBYAN COASTLANDS
All three synoptic gospels name Simon of Cyrene as the person compelled to carry Jesus' cross (Matthew 27.32/Mark 15.21/Luke 23.26).

1. Cyrene was the capital of the Roman province of Cyrenaica (modern Libya plus Crete). Located about ten miles from the Mediterranean coast, the city was surrounded by a fertile area producing grain, olive oil, wool, and—its most famous product—silphium, a spice prized for both medicinal and culinary uses. It was second only to Alexandria as a cultural center of northern Africa, and Jews were an important part of its population. Acts 6.9 suggests that Jews returning from Cyrene and Alexandria were both numerous and prosperous enough to have their own synagogue in Jerusalem.

4. Matthew 10.38, 16.24/Mark 8.34/Luke 9.23, 14.27.

*Tune*: BICKFORD is named for a close friend of the composer whose career as a writer and director was prematurely cut short by fatal brain tumors. It first appeared with two texts in *The Hymnal 1982.*

## 24. MIXED LIKE WEEDS IN WHEATFIELDS
This text applies Jesus' parable of the wheat and tares (Matthew 13.24-43) to the complexities of our personalities and the mixedness of even our best motives.

1. Cf. John 2.10; Matthew 7.6, 13.44-46.

2. Matthew 5.39/Luke 6.29; Matthew 5.3-7.

*Tune*: DARNEL attempts to reflect the text through blended tonalities and frequent suspensions. The tune name is the term used for the undesirable plants in several modern translations of the parable (New English Bible, Revised English Bible, Jerusalem Bible, and New Jerusalem Bible).

## 25. TAKE US AS WE ARE, O GOD
This text is constructed around the fourfold shape of the Eucharist identified by Dom Gregory Dix in *The Shape of the Liturgy* (London, 1945; rpt. New York, 1982): *take, bless, break, give*. It explores the correspondences between the two senses of the label "Body of Christ": consecrated Bread/ baptized People.

3. The feeding of the five thousand is described in Matthew 14.15- 21/Mark 6.35-44/Luke 9.12-17/John 6.1-15 and that of the four thousand in Matthew 15.32-39/Mark 8.1 10. That "the dead are raised" is among the Messianic signs of Jesus' ministry reported to John the Baptist (Matthew 11.5/Luke 7.22). Instances of Jesus' reviving of the dead include the daughter of the ruler of the synagogue (Matthew 9.18-19,23-26/Mark 5.21-24a,35-43/Luke 8.40-42a,49-56), the son of the widow of Nain (Luke 7.11-17), and especially the raising of Lazarus (John 11.1-44).

4. Matthew 5.13-16, 13.33/Luke 13.20-21.

*Tune*: ENDLESS FEAST is aptly named, for this chant-like tune never resolves to the tonic, yet it is strong, rich, and nourishing.

## 26-27. TRAVELLERS' CHILD LAID IN A MANGER
This text was commissioned for the 1993 national conference of the Association of Diocesan Liturgy and Music Commissions of the Episcopal Church, held in Jackson, Mississippi. The theme of the conference was "All Find a Welcome: The Hospitality of God in Liturgy and Life."

1. Scripture allusions in this stanza include: Luke 2.1-7; Matthew 2.13-15; Luke 2.41-51; Philippians 2.5-11.

2. The opening line summarizes John 2.1-11, and lines 3-4 are based on John 4.3-42. No specific healing is intended by line 2; a helpful interpretation of the importance of Jesus' reputation as a healer can be found in Marcus J. Borg, *Jesus: A New Vision* (San Francisco: Harper & Row, 1987), pp. 60-67.

3. For Jesus' frequent use of the Garden of Gethsemane as a place for prayer, rest, and fellowship with the disciples, see Matthew 26.30,36/Mark 14.26,32/Luke 22.39-40/John 18.1-2. The arrangements for securing a place for celebrating the Passover are described in Matthew 26.17-19/Mark 14.12-16/Luke 22.7-13. All four gospels mention the release of Barabbas: Matthew 17.15-26/ Mark 15.6-15/Luke 23.13-25/John 18.38b-40, 19.12-16. Though

Matthew is the only gospel to indicate that the tomb belonged to Joseph of Arimathea, all four name him as the person who oversaw the burial of Jesus (Matthew 27.57-60/Mark 15.42-46/Luke 23.50-53/John 19.38-42).

4. See Luke 24.13-35 for the Emmaus story, which is followed immediately by Jesus' appearance to the assembled disciples (Luke 24.36-43; cf. John 20.19-20). The post-Resurrection appearance by the Sea of Tiberias (or Galilee) is told only in John 21.1-14. The final line of the stanza alludes to Matthew 25.31-46.

*Tunes*: MISSISSIPPI, as its name implies, was commissioned for the previously-noted conference in Jackson, Mississippi. This lush setting also forms the basis of an anthem version of this hymn titled "In All These You Welcomed Me" (Augsburg Fortress 11-10661). REFUGEE offers an alternative, slightly brighter but still quite lyrical setting. It is especially interesting to observe the points of similarity and difference in these two tunes, each composed as an expression of patterns implicit in the text.

## 28. WE SEE IN JESUS A LOVE BEYOND TELLING

This text was sparked by a paragraph in John H. Snow's *The Impossible Vocation: Ministry in the Mean Time* (Cambridge, MA: Cowley Publications, 1988), pp. 88-89:

> The atonement, what Jesus accomplished in reconciling us to himself, lay in becoming one of us, perfectly human (that is, perfectly imperfect), and acting as a person free to love even at the risk of death, ignoring the claims of Satan even though he, like us, was mortal and subject to the same mortal fate of suffering and death. Through the cross Jesus overcame the power of death. . . . Sacrificial love, love that makes holy by risking and spending itself, overcomes the kingdom of death, the rule of entropy, and frees the human race from its bondage of fear.

1. This stanza includes allusions to Philippians 2.5-11, Matthew 1.23, John 1.14.

4. Baptism joins us to Christ's death and resurrection, recalled and proclaimed in the Eucharist.

5. Cf. no 43, "Have we any gift worth giving."

*Tune*: O QUANTA QUALIA represents several centuries and various musical styles. The earliest form of the Mode VI melody appeared in the *Paris Antiphoner* of 1681. Thomas Helmore reworked the melody into a consistent dactylic rhythm as a setting for John Mason Neale's translation of Peter Abelard's text, "O quanta, qualia sunt illa sabbata" ("O what their joy and their glory must be"). The harmonization used here was introduced in the Appendix of *Hymns Ancient & Modern* in 1868.

## 29. WERE TADPOLES TO FLY OR FIREFLIES TO SING

This text attempts to recapture some of the wonder and mystery of Christ's death and resurrection in oblique, symbolic language.

*Tune*: The tune name ROODSONG is intended to recall the great Old English mystical poem, "The Dream of the Rood," wherein the cross itself is endowed with the ability to describe Christ's crucifixion and resurrection.

## 30. WHEN DOUBT AND FEAR IMPALE OUR HOPES

This text was commissioned for an offertory anthem at the Consecration of M. Thomas Shaw, SSJE, as Bishop Coadjutor of the Diocese of Massachusetts, September 24, 1994. At his request the central theme of the liturgy was the cross.

*Tune*: MARVIL is derived from the composer's anthem setting commissioned for this consecration. Note especially how the refrain quotes the tune ROCKINGHAM (the customary Episcopal tune for "When I survey the wondrous cross," which the congregation sang at the conclusion of the choir's anthem). The tune name is the bishop's first name.

## 31. WHO IS MY NEIGHBOR, LORD?

This hymn was written in collaboration with the composer as an entry in a contest sponsored by Christian Aid to celebrate their 50th birthday. There were nearly 400 entries, and we did not win. But we enjoyed creating this hymn based on the parable of the Good Samaritan (Luke 10.25-37).

*Tune*: DAVID EARLE is designed for flexibility in presentation. It may be sung in unison or 4-part harmony, accompanied or unaccompanied, with off-beat handclaps to enhance the rhythm, with keyboard and/or guitars. The tune bears the given names of the composer's youngest son.

## 32. AS SIX-WINGED SERAPHS VOLLEYED PRAISE

This hymn is a reflection on Isaiah 6.1-8.

*Tune*: TALLIS' LAMENTATION first appeared in John Day's *The Whole Booke of Psalmes* (London, 1562), where it is headed "A Prayer. M. Talys." It provides a setting for the metrical prayer "O Lord, in thee is all my trust" (titled "A Lamentation") customarily appended to the Sternhold and Hopkins metrical psalter.

## 33-34. BEYOND THE BEAUTY AND THE AWE

This text attempts to deal with the often painful and disorienting disparity between daily life and the worship of the church.

     5.  Matthew 5.13-16, 13.33/Luke 13.20-21.

*Tunes*: Both these tunes grew out of a Hymnwriting Conference at St. Olaf College in June 1995 sponsored by the Hymn Society in the United States and Canada. RUFINOT (the composer's wife's surname) was featured as one of the best tunes from the Conference in a report to the Hymn Society at its July 1995 meeting in San Diego. DOWNING is named for Edith Sinclair Downing, another participant in the conference.

## 35. BREATH OF GOD, LIFE-BEARING WIND

This hymn seeks to recapture the corollary meanings of "wind" and "breath" in the biblical words usually translated as "spirit": *ruach* in Hebrew and *pneuma* in Greek.

1. Genesis 1.1-2; Psalm 104.30.

2. Cf. the third paragraph of the Nicene Creed: "We believe in the Holy Spirit, the Lord, the giver of life, who proceeds from the Father and the Son. With the Father and the Son he is worshiped and glorified. He has spoken through the Prophets" (Book of Common Prayer, p. 359).

3. Acts 2.1-11,43-47.

4. St. Augustine said, "Whoever sings prays twice."

*Tune*: BINGHAM was composed for *The Hymnal 1982* as a setting for W. H. Vanstone's text, "Morning glory, starlit sky." The tune name honors the composer's composition teacher, Seth Bingham.

## 36. BY WATER AND THE SPIRIT

This text was commissioned for the 1994 General Convention of the Episcopal Church.

Refrain: This is based on Proper Preface 3. Of God the Holy Spirit: "For by water and the Holy Spirit you have made us a new people in Jesus Christ our Lord, to show forth your glory in all the world" (Book of Common Prayer, p. 378).

1. Genesis 1.1-2.24.

2. Galatians 4.4; Matthew 9.10-13/Mark 2.15-17/Luke 5.29-32, 15.1-2.

3. Acts 2.1-11.

4. Ephesians 4.1-6.

*Tune*: Two tunes were connected with the commission mentioned earlier. HOLY PEOPLE was the composer's initial response to the text. After receiving it, however, the commissioning committee asked for a tune that could be accompanied by guitars. So she composed a second tune, BROWNING (named for the Rt. Rev. Edmond L. Browning, Presiding Bishop of the

Episcopal Church), which was used at the convention.

## 37. DARK AND COMELY, EVENING VEILS

This text represents an effort to write a positive hymn for evening, in contrast to the dominant tradition regarding night and darkness as malevolent.

1. The opening line echoes Song of Solomon 1.5 (especially the wording of the Revised Standard Version). The second half of this stanza is an abbreviated paraphrase of the ancient evening hymn *Phos hilaron*; for a fuller paraphrase see *A Year of Grace*, pp. 120-121, and *To Sing God's Praise*, nos. 19-20.

2. Cf. Psalm 19.2b.

3. The first half of this stanza is based on a prayer appointed for Evening Prayer and Compline (Book of Common Prayer, pp. 71, 124, 134): "Keep watch, dear Lord, with those who work, or watch, or weep this night, and give your angels charge over those who sleep. Tend the sick, Lord Christ; give rest to the weary, bless the dying, soothe the suffering, pity the afflicted, shield the joyous; and all for your love's sake. Amen." Lines 5-6 paraphrase the Compline antiphon for the *Nunc dimittis*: "Guide us waking, O Lord, and guard us sleeping; that awake we may watch with Christ, and asleep we may rest in peace" (Book of Common Prayer, p. 134).

*Tune*: The unison pentatonic melody STOOKEY first appeared in *Hymnal Supplement II* (Carol Stream, IL: Agape, 1987) as a setting for Charles Wesley's text "O the depth of love divine," with which it later appeared in *The United Methodist Hymnal*. The tune is named for Laurence Hall Stookey, who served as the chair of the worship resources subcommittee for that hymnal. The alternative tune BORROWED LIGHT by Dave Brubeck can be found with Rusty Edwards' text "As the Moon is to the Sun" (*The Yes of the Heart* [Carol Stream, IL: Hope Publishing Co., 1993], no. 1).

## 38. FAITH BEGINS BY LETTING GO

This hymn affirms that faith is not a state of being but a process of becoming what we are called to be in relationship to God, other people, and the world.

*Tune*: The composer refers to JULION as "a generic tune." It was composed in 1974 and first appeared in *The David Hurd Hymnary* (Chicago: GIA, 1983) with Vincent Stuckey Stratton Coles' "Ye who claim the faith of Jesus," a pairing that has been continued in several hymnals. The tune is named for John Julion Mann, a friend of the composer.

## 39. FRIEND OF THE STREETWALKER, BEGGAR, AND CHILD

This text grapples with the disparity between our human impulse to exclude those who are different from us and the clear witness of scripture and tradition that God's nature is to embrace and welcome them.

1. In Matthew 21.31-32 Jesus praises the repentance of tax collectors and prostitutes. There is also a long tradition of understanding the sinful woman of Luke 7.36-50 as a prostitute, though her sin is not specified. The beggars to whom Jesus responds often suffer from some physical impairment, especially blindness (see Mark 10.46-52, Luke 18.35-43, John 9.1-41). All three synoptic gospels include Jesus' rebuke to the disciples who were trying to keep children from reaching him (Matthew 19.13-15/Mark 10.13-16/ Luke 18.17).

4. The triune nature of God means that the image of God in human beings is most clearly revealed in community rather than in individuality.

*Tune*: As its name shows, MYRRH-BEARING MARY was composed as a setting for Rae Whitney's text "Myrrh-bearing Mary from Magdala came" and was first published in *The Alfred V. Fedak Hymnary* (Accord, NY: Selah Publishing Co., 1990).

## 40. GOD BE WITH US WHEN WE GATHER HERE

This text was commissioned for the 150th anniversary of the founding of Emmanuel Episcopal Church in Weston, Connecticut. It uses the explication of "Emmanuel" from Matthew 1.23 (which is inscribed on the wall above the reredos of this church) as the basis for a threefold prayer for God's presence as the people of the parish come together, join in worship, and resume their lives in the world.

*Tune*: EMMANUEL PARISH, WESTON is derived from the composer's anthem setting for this text (Selah 410-642), which was composed for the occasion previously mentioned.

## 41. GOD OF COSMOS AND OF ATOM

This hymn was written while attending a retreat on Celtic spirituality led by the Rev. Canon A. M. Allchin at Emery House, a retreat center of the Society of St. John the Evangelist. It attempts to bring together a number of themes featured in Canon Allchin's reflections. Its structure mirrors the strong Trinitarian grounding of this spiritual tradition.

1. Celtic spirituality emphasizes the connectedness of all creation and celebrates God's presence to things small as well as great.

2. The opening lines of this stanza are intended to recall the intricate interwoven patterns of zoomorphic tracery characteristic

of Celtic art.

3. Images of the cross are important to numerous stories of Celtic saints, and some of the finest testimonies to the blending of Celtic faith and art are the "high crosses" of the crossroads and markets, many of which are now moved indoors to preserve them.

*Tune*: In tribute to my Welsh forebears, this text was written specifically for AR HYD Y NOS, a Welsh harp melody probably from the 17th century. (The Welsh tune name means literally "on length of night.") The present harmonization is attributed to Luther Orlando Emerson (ca. 1906).

## 42. GOD OF WOMBING, GOD OF BIRTH
As a counterbalance to portrayals of God's wrath and judgment, this hymn celebrates the nurturing nature of God.

1. Genesis 2.7, 1.26-27.

4. John 8.12, 9.5; 11.25, 14.6.

*Tunes*: SAVANNAH (also known as HERRNHUT) is a tune of Moravian derivation taken over by John Wesley for his *Foundery Collection* (London, 1742). The present tune name and harmonization originated with Thomas Butts' *Harmonica Sacra* (London, 1756). Although Wesley had served in Savannah, Georgia, in 1736-1737, there is no known connection between the tune name and that city. The alternative tune THE CALL (adapted from one of Ralph Vaughan Williams' *Five Mystical Songs*) is available in many hymnals.

## 43. HAVE WE ANY GIFT WORTH GIVING
Commissioned for the 189th General Synod of the Reformed Church in America in June 1995, this hymn is based (as requested) on Romans 12.1-2. The meter chosen is the same as GENEVA 42, one of the most cherished tunes in this singing tradition.

*Tune*: COSTLY GIFTS, commissioned for the same occasion, deftly adapts the melodic shapes and rhythms of GENEVA 42, with just enough changes to seem fresh and enough similarity to encourage singing at first encounter.

## 44. IN COMPANY WITH EVERY AGE
This text was commissioned for the 50th anniversary of St. Columb's Episcopal Church, Jackson, Mississippi. The four stanzas are an acrostic on Iona, the island where the namesake saint established his famous monastery. The content of each stanza reflects the shape of the Eucharistic liturgy: gathering for worship and reading scripture; the proclamation of the sermon and the affirmation of the Creed; the prayers of the people; receiving Communion and returning to daily living.

*Tune*: Familiar and well-loved, ST. COLUMBA seemed an inevitable choice for a tune. This traditional Irish melody was first collected by George Petri around 1855 and went through various changes, arriving at essentially its present form in Charles Villiers Stanford's harmonization (the first to use the memorable triplet) for the *English Hymnal* (London, 1906).

## 45. MIGHTY GOD WHO CALLED CREATION
Commissioned in 1991 for the dedication of the renovated worship space of St. Mark's Episcopal Church in Jacksonville, Florida, this text is an acrostic on that saint's name. Each of the first three stanzas invokes one of the Persons of the Trinity, and the final one is addressed to the whole Godhead. In many ways it is a Sunday hymn because it recalls the three principal events celebrated by worshiping on the first day of the week: Creation, Resurrection, and Pentecost (though not in that order here).

1. Genesis 1.1-2.25.

2. Acts 2.1-11.

3. The image of the vineyard was central to Israel's self-understanding (see Isaiah 5.7; Psalm 80.8-19). Jesus uses vineyard images in several important parables concerning what it means to live under God's sovereignty (Matthew 20.1-16; 21.28-32; 21.33-43/Mark 12.1-11/Luke 20.9-18).

*Tune*: In working through the available tunes in this meter, the leaders of the parish music program settled on RUSTINGTON. It was a wise choice, for the text is carried well by this tune named for the village in Sussex where the composer spent the latter part of his life. It first appeared in *The Westminster Abbey Hymn-Book* (London, 1897) with Benjamin Webb's "Praise the Rock of our salvation."

## 46. NOT ALONE, BUT TWO BY TWO
This text rises out of a deep conviction that we misrepresent the nature of God in our customary patterns of ministry and evangelism. Secular emphasis on individual achievement, with its inherent assumption of competition rather than cooperation, has conditioned us to expect sole leaders and lone missionaries. Historically, these people have been primarily male, entrenching a pattern of patriarchy that has only recently begun to be recognized and (slowly) dismantled. But I believe that honoring the gifts of women for ordained leadership is only the beginning of recovering a truly healing model of shared ministry rooted in an understanding of the community as the fundamental unit of Christian witness.

1. Matthew 10.1,9-14/Mark 6.7-13/Luke 9.1-6, 10:1-9.

*Tune*: TURNBERRY was composed for "Sing of God made manifest" (*A Year of Grace*, p. 43) and was first published in *The Roy Hopp Hymnary* (Accord,NY: Selah Publishing Co., 1990). The tune name commemorates a memorable birthday the composer spent on that golf course in Scotland. The suggested alternative, Joseph Parry's ABERYSTWYTH, has become perhaps the best-known Welsh hymntune in the world and is widely available.

### 47. O BOUNDLESS GOD, WHO CHOSE TO BIND

St. Paul's Episcopal Church in Woodbury, Connecticut, commissioned this text in 1990 for their 250th anniversary celebration, with a request that it deal with the theme of covenant. Each stanza explores this subject with regard to one of the Persons of the Trinity.

*Tunes*: COVENANT was composed by the parish's organist and choirmaster for this celebration. The pentatonic Scottish tune CANDLER, also known as YE BANKS AND BRAES from its use as a setting for Robert Burns' poem opening with that phrase, can be found in several recent hymnals.

### 48-49. O GOD IN WHOM ALL LIFE BEGINS

This hymn was commissioned in 1990 to be used at the installation of the Rev. Susan Huizenga as the pastor of the Rochester Reformed Church in Accord, New York.

*Tunes*: As its name implies, ACCORD was commissioned for this occasion. Although it can be understood as the noun meaning "agreement or harmony" (and therefore having the accent on the second syllable), the tune name is properly pronounced as local people call the town: AC'-cord. RITTER was composed for use at the service in 1993 when Erba, David, and Jonathan Ritter were admitted as a Provisional Chapter Family of the Community of Celebration in Aliquippa, Pennsylvania.

### 50. O GOD WHO PLANTED EDEN WELL

This text was commissioned for use in Duke University Chapel on February 16, 1992, during my visit as Artist in Residence at the Divinity School. Because the appointed readings for the day included Jeremiah 17.5-10 and Psalm 1, the recurring image of "a tree planted by water" suggested this exploration of plant imagery associated with the Persons of the Trinity.

1. Genesis 1.11-12, 2.9, 3.1-24; Psalm 34.8
2. Exodus 3.1-6 (with an anticipation of Acts 2.1-11).
3. Matthew 21.7-9/Mark 11.7-10/Luke 19.35-40/John 12.12-19; Matthew 26.30,47-56/Mark 14.26,43-52/Luke 22.39,47-54a/John 18.1-2.

4. Jeremiah 17.8, Psalm 1.3; 1 Corinthians 13.13.

*Tunes*: FOREST GREEN was adapted by Ralph Vaughan Williams for the *English Hymnal* (London, 1906). He transcribed the ballad tune from the melody of "The ploughboy's dream" as sung by a Mr. Garman of Forest Green near Ockley in Surrey.

## 51. PRAISE GOD WHO GIVES ALL BLESSINGS BIRTH
This gender-free doxology was written to provide a compatible final stanza for the revision of Thomas Ken's "All praise to thee, my God, this night" in *The New Century Hymnal* (Cleveland: Pilgrim Press, 1995).

*Tunes*: OLD HUNDREDTH takes its name from its pairing with William Kethe's metrical version of Psalm 100, available to English-speaking congregations since at least 1560. The tune itself can be traced to the French metrical psalter *Pseumes octante trois de David* (Geneva, 1551), and may be the work of Louis Bourgeois. In congregations where a doxology is sung weekly, some variety can be introduced by using TALLIS' CANON as an alternative setting. Another option would be to use LASST UNS ERFREUEN, adding alleluias at the appropriate points after the second and fourth lines.

## 52. TILL ALL THE JAILS ARE EMPTY
This text is a reflection on and application of the passage from Isaiah 61.1-2 and 58.6 which Jesus is reported to have read in his first visit to the synagogue in Nazareth after his baptism and temptation (Luke 4.14-30). If this Messianic passage shaped Jesus' ministry, what does it imply for Christians today?

*Tune*: Composed especially for this text and this collection, WORK TO DO effectively draws on the rhythms and harmonies of "worldly" music to convey the urgency of Christian witness. The alternative tune ANTHEA appears with this text in Hope Publishing Company's *Supplement 96*.

## 53. WE COME, O CHRIST, AS PEOPLE SEEKING
This text was commissioned by Christian Theological Seminary, Indianapolis, and was first sung at a festival of my hymns there on March 10, 1993. In writing this hymn for seminarians, the informing biblical event was the appeal to Jesus for special consideration of James and John (Matthew 20.20-28/Mark 10.35-45).

2. Matthew 20.22/Mark 10.38; with an allusion to the denominational logo of the Christian Church (Disciples of Christ), who sponsor the seminary that commissioned the hymn.

3. The third line adapts line 40 of John Donne's "Good Friday 1613. Riding Westward."

*Tune*: RATHERVUE connects this hymn with another seminary, the Episcopal Theological Seminary of the Southwest in Austin, Texas, where both composer and author, along with four other people engaged in the making of hymns, were Visiting Fellows during two memorable weeks in February 1995. The tune name commemorates the street on which the seminary is located. The widely-available alternative, Georg Neumark's WER NUR DEN LIEBEN GOTT (also known as NEUMARK), was used for the text's premiere.

## 54. WE SING FOR ALL THE UNSUNG SAINTS
This hymn was conceived as a simpler and non-militaristic alternative to William Walsham How's "For all the saints."

> 2.  1 Peter 2.4-10; Revelation 5.6-14.
>
> 3.  Isaiah 56.5; Ecclesiasticus (Sirach) 44.9-15.

*Tune*: The ballad melody which has become the hymntune KINGSFOLD was introduced to the arranger through its use in Lucy Broadwood's *English County Songs* (London, 1893) as a setting for "Dives and Lazarus." It has also been associated with the carol "Job," and is known in Ireland as THE STAR OF THE COUNTY DOWN. When Vaughan Williams chose it as the setting for Horatio Bonar's "I heard the voice of Jesus say" in the *English Hymnal* (London, 1906), he assigned its present name to commemorate the village in northwest Sussex where he first heard the tune.

## 55. WHAT HAVE YOU HERE TO EAT?
Most of this text was written in the Toronto airport during an extended afternoon wait for a return flight from the 1993 conference of the Hymn Society in the United States and Canada. It is a reflection on Jesus' question to the disciples in Luke 24.41. The episode in which it occurs had been read in two different contexts that morning, and the question haunted me.

> 1.  Luke 24.36-43.
>
> 4.  For a fuller development of the fourfold shape of the Eucharist, see no. 25, "Take us as we are, O God."

*Tune*: DINBYCH appeared in the composer's collection *Llyfr Tônau Cynulleidfaol Cenedlaethol Cymru* (1887-1892), and is somewhat abridged here. The tune name is the Welsh form of Denbigh, the principal market town in the upper part of the Vale of Clwyd.

## 56. WHEN EVERYTHING SEEMS POSSIBLE
This hymn was triggered by reading a report of Vaclav Havel's speech when awarded the Liberty Medal in Philadelphia on July 4, 1994. Havel described Western culture as having entered a postmodern phase where "everything is possible and almost nothing is certain."

3. See Luke 15.20.

*Tune*: CASADAY has been adapted from the composer's anthem setting of this text, commissioned for use at the January 1995 convention of the Episcopal Diocese of Mississippi. The tune name perpetuates the intention of that composition to honor Leslie Casaday, founding director of the Mississippi Conference on Church Music and Liturgy. The alternative tune by Thomas Tallis, THE THIRD TUNE (also called THIRD MODE MELODY) appears in many hymnals.

## 57. WHEN WE FEEL DEFEATED

In 1994 the Hymn Society in the United States and Canada initiated a search for new texts for JESU, MEINE FREUDE and EARTH AND ALL STARS. I had begun to think about the former tune, then was asked to be a judge for the competition, so I put the task aside until the judging was completed. The resulting text attempts to listen to the music rather than to follow the patterns of Johann Franck's poem. The original rhyme scheme *aabaab[c] cdd* (taking line 7's midline rhyme into account) has become *abcabcdea*, reflecting the repeat in the tune, as well as Bach's practice of giving the final phrase the same shape as the opening one (see *The Worshiping Church*, no. 119, and *The United Methodist Hymnal*, no. 532).

*Tune*: JESU, MEINE FREUDE was first published in the composer's *Praxis Pietatis Melica* (Berlin, 1653) as a setting for Johann Franck's text beginning with these words, variously translated into English as "Jesus, priceless treasure" (following Catherine Winkworth) or "Jesus, all my gladness" (following Arthur Wellesley Wotherspoon).

# Jndexes

The Indexes are for this book *New Psalms and Hymns and Spiritual Songs* (New) as well as Carl P. Daw Jr.'s two other books published by Hope Publishing Company: *A Year of Grace* (Year) and *To Sing God's Praise* (Sing).

# SCRIPTURE INDEX

| 126 | New 16 |
|---|---|
| 130 | Year 59 |
| 133 | New 8 |
| 137.1-6 | Year 141; New 3 |
| 139.1-16 | New 5,6 |
| 145.17 | Year 117; Sing 33,34 |
| 149 | New 13 |

**Song of Solomon**

| 1.5 | New 37 |
|---|---|

**Isaiah**

| 5.7 | New 45 |
|---|---|
| 6.1-8 | New 32 |
| 6.3 | Year 119; Sing 35,36 |
| 9.2 | Year 23 |
| 9.6 | Year 23 |
| 9.7 | Year 13 |
| 11.1 | Year 17,31; Sing 3,4 |
| 11.10 | Year 17; Sing 3,4 |
| 11.6-9 | Year 21,167 |
| 12.2-6 | Year 147; Sing 31,32 |
| 35.1-2,5-6 | Year 21 |
| 35.10 | Year 93 |
| 38.14 | Year 85,87 |
| 40.3 | Year 17,19; Sing 3,4 |
| 40.3-4 | Year 21 |
| 42.6 | Year 145; Sing 17,18 |
| 49.1 | New 5,6 |
| 49.6 | Year 145; Sing 17,18 |
| 53.3-5 | Year 23 |
| 55.6-11 | Year 57; Sing 23,24 |
| 55.10-11 | New 21 |
| 56.5 | New 54 |
| 56.7 | Year 101 |
| 58.6 | New 52 |
| 58.7 | Year 39 |
| 59.11 | Year 85,87 |
| 60.1-3,11A,14C,18-19 | Year 47; Sing 21,22 |
| 61.1-2 | Year 52 |

**Jeremiah**

| 1.5 | New 5,6 |
|---|---|
| 10.7 | Year 117; Sing 33,34 |
| 11.5 | Year 17; Sing 3,4 |
| 17.8 | New 50 |
| 31.31-34 | Year 53,59 |

**Ezekiel**

| 8.17 | Year 15 |
|---|---|
| 16.4 | Year 31 |
| 37.1-14 | Year 59 |

**Hosea**

| 11.1 | Year 39 |
|---|---|

**Micah**

| 4.1-4 | Year 21 |
|---|---|
| 7.20 | Year 17; Sing 3,4 |

**Zephaniah**

| 3.14-20 | Year 21 |
|---|---|

**Malachi**

| 3.1 | Year 17; Sing 3,4 |
|---|---|

## APOCRYPHA

**Wisdom of Solomon**

| 7.4 | Year 31 |
|---|---|

**Sirach (Ecclesiasticus)**

| 44.9-15 | New 54 |
|---|---|

**Prayer of Manasseh**

| 1-2,4,6-7,11-15 | Year 55; Sing 27,28 |
|---|---|

**Prayer of Azaraiah and
  Song of the Three Jews**

| 1-68 | New 1 |
|---|---|
| 29-34 | Year 113; Sing 9,10 |
| 35-65 | Year 111; Sing 13,14 |

## NEW TESTAMENT

**Matthew**

| 1.13-15 | Year 39 |
|---|---|
| 1.18-2.23 | Year 23 |
| 1.23 | New 28,40 |
| 2.1-12 | Year 43 |
| 2.13-15 | New 26,27 |
| 2.21 | Year 31 |
| 3.1-12 | Year 19 |
| 3.13-17 | Year 43,45,127 |
| 4.1-2 | Year 45 |
| 4.23-25 | Year 39 |
| 5.3-7 | New 24 |
| 5.13-16 | New 25,33,34 |
| 5.39 | New 24 |
| 6.25-34 | New 22 |
| 6.33 | Year 97 |
| 7.6 | New 24 |
| 9.10-13 | New 36 |
| 9.18-19,23-26 | New 25 |
| 9.35 | Year 39 |
| 10.1,9-14 | New 46 |
| 10.38 | New 23 |
| 11.5 | New 25 |
| 11.28-30 | Year 155 |
| 13.3-9,18-43 | New 21 |

| | |
|---|---|
| 13.24-33 | New 24 |
| 13.33 | New 33,34 |
| 13.44-46 | New 24 |
| 13.55 | Year 155 |
| 14.15-21 | New 25 |
| 15.32-39 | New 25 |
| 16.13-20 | Year 139 |
| 16.24 | New 23 |
| 17.1-13 | Year 43,49; New 18,19,20 |
| 17.14-23 | Year 49; New 18,29,20 |
| 19.13-15 | New 39 |
| 20.1-16 | New 45 |
| 20.20-28 | New 53 |
| 21.7-9 | Year 65; New 50 |
| 21.12-14 | Year 101 |
| 21.28-43 | New 45 |
| 21.31-32 | New 39 |
| 22.1-10 | Year 161 |
| 22.15-22 | New 17 |
| 22.37-40 | Year 105 |
| 25.1-13 | Year 15 |
| 25.31-46 | Year 39,119; Sing 35,36; New 25,26,27 |
| 26.17-19 | New 26,27 |
| 26.26-29 | Year 67 |
| 26.30 | New 1,26,27,50 |
| 26.36 | New 26,27 |
| 26.47-56 | New 50 |
| 27.15-26 | New 26,27 |
| 27.27-31 | Year 65 |
| 27.32 | New 23 |
| 27.33-44 | Year 65 |
| 27.45-56 | Year 71 |
| 27.46 | Year 65; New 1 |
| 27.57-60 | New 26,27 |

**Mark**

| | |
|---|---|
| 1.2-8 | Year 19 |
| 1.9-11 | Year 43,45,127 |
| 1.12-13 | Year 45 |
| 1.35-39 | Year 39 |
| 2.15-17 | New 36 |
| 4.2-9,13-20 | New 21 |
| 5.21-24a,35-43 | New 25 |
| 6.3 | Year 155 |
| 6.7-13 | New 46 |
| 6.35-44 | New 25 |
| 8.1-10 | New 25 |
| 8.27-30 | Year 139 |
| 8.34 | New 23 |
| 9.2-9 | Year 43,49; New 18,19,20 |
| 9.14-32 | Year 49; New 18,19,20 |
| 10.13-16 | New 39 |
| 10.35-45 | New 53 |
| 10.46-52 | New 39 |
| 11.7-10 | Year 65; New 50 |

| | |
|---|---|
| 11.15-19 | Year 101 |
| 12.1-11 | New 45 |
| 12.13-17 | New 17 |
| 12.29-31 | Year 105 |
| 14.12-16 | New 26,27 |
| 14.22-25 | Year 67 |
| 14.26 | New 1,26,27,50 |
| 14.32 | New 26,27 |
| 14.43-52 | New 50 |
| 15.6-15 | New 26,27 |
| 15.16-20 | Year 65 |
| 15.21 | New 23 |
| 15.22-32 | Year 65 |
| 15.33-41 | Year 71 |
| 15.34 | New 1 |
| 15.42-46 | New 26,27 |

**Luke**

| | |
|---|---|
| 1.20-22,63-64 | Year 17; Sing 3,4 |
| 1.26-38 | Year 27 |
| 1.26-2.40 | Year 23 |
| 1.28 | Year 25; Sing 15,16 |
| 1.46-55 | Year 25; Sing 15,16 |
| 1.51-52 | Year 77; Sing 25,26 |
| 1.68-79 | Year 17; Sing 3,4 |
| 2.1-7 | New 26,27 |
| 2.7 | Year 31 |
| 2.8-14 | Year 129 |
| 2.9-11 | Year 33 |
| 2.14 | Year 31,35; Sing 7,8 |
| 2.15 | Year 33 |
| 2.21,30 | Year 31 |
| 2.29-32 | Year 145; Sing 17,18 |
| 2.41-51 | New 26,27 |
| 3.1-20 | Year 19 |
| 3.21-22 | Year 43,45, 127 |
| 4.1-2 | Year 45 |
| 4.14-30 | New 52 |
| 4.42-44 | Year 39 |
| 5.29-32 | New 36 |
| 6.29 | New 24 |
| 7.11-17 | New 25 |
| 7.22 | New 25 |
| 7.36-50 | New 39 |
| 8.4-8,11-15 | New 21 |
| 8.40-42a,49-56 | New 25 |
| 9.1-6 | New 46 |
| 9.12-17 | New 25 |
| 9.18-22 | Year 139 |
| 9.23 | New 23 |
| 9.28-36 | Year 43,49; New 18,19,20 |
| 9.37-45 | Year 49; New 18,19,20 |
| 10.1-9 | New 46 |
| 10.25-37 | New 31 |
| 10.27 | Year 105 |
| 12.22-31 | New 22 |

| | |
|---|---|
| 13.20-21 | New 25,33,34 |
| 14.16-24 | Year 161 |
| 14.27 | New 23 |
| 15.1-2 | New 36 |
| 15.20 | New 55 |
| 18.17 | New 39 |
| 18.35-43 | New 39 |
| 19.35-40 | Year 65; New 50 |
| 19.45-48 | Year 101 |
| 20.20-26 | New 17 |
| 22.7-13 | New 26,27 |
| 22.14-20 | Year 67 |
| 22.39-40 | New 26,27; New 50 |
| 23.13-25 | New 26,27 |
| 23.26 | New 23 |
| 23.33-43 | Year 65 |
| 23.44-49 | Year 71 |
| 23.47-54a | New 50 |
| 23.50-53 | New 26,27 |
| 24.13-35 | Year 81; New 26,27 |
| 24.36b-48 | Year 81; New 26,27,55 |

**John**

| | |
|---|---|
| 1.1-3 | Year 155 |
| 1.4-5 | Year 121; Sing 19,20 |
| 1.1-18 | Year 23 |
| 1.14 | Year 37,67,155; New 1,28 |
| 1.18 | Year 37 |
| 1.19-29,36 | Year 19 |
| 1.32-33 | Year 127 |
| 1.35-41 | Year 143 |
| 1.51 | Year 129 |
| 2.1-11 | Year 43; New 26,27 |
| 2.10 | New 24 |
| 2.13-17 | Year 101 |
| 3.16 | Year 105; New 25 |
| 3.16-17 | Year 37,165 |
| 4.3-42 | New 26,27 |
| 5.22 | Year 119; Sing 35,36 |
| 6.1-15 | New 25 |
| 6.8-9 | Year 143 |
| 6.35-38 | Year 31 |
| 8.12 | New 42 |
| 8.82 | Year 137 |
| 9.1-41 | New 39 |
| 9.5 | New 42 |
| 10.10 | Year 163 |
| 10.11-16 | Year 127 |
| 10.28 | Year 31 |
| 11.1-44 | Year 163; New 25 |
| 11.20 | Year 79 |
| 11.25 | Year 31; New 42 |
| 12.12-19 | Year 65; New 50 |
| 12.20-22 | Year 143 |
| 14.2,5 | Year 137 |
| 14.6 | Year 31; New 42 |

| | |
|---|---|
| 14.16-17 | Year 119; Sing 35,36 |
| 14.26 | Year 127 |
| 15.1 | Year 31 |
| 15.1-5 | Year 85 |
| 15.26 | Year 119; Sing 35,36 |
| 17.1-26 | Year 81 |
| 18.1-2 | New 26,27; New 50 |
| 18.38b-40 | New 26,27 |
| 19.1-3 | Year 65 |
| 19.12-16 | New 26,27 |
| 19.17-24 | Year 65 |
| 19.30 | Year 65 |
| 19.38-42 | New 26,27 |
| 20.19-23 | Year 87; New 26,27 |
| 20.19-31 | Year 79,81 |
| 20.22-23 | Year 85 |
| 21.1-14 | New 26,27 |
| 21.11-14 | Year 81 |
| 21.15-17 | Year 139 |

**Acts**

| | |
|---|---|
| 1.8 | Year 53,85,127 |
| 1.13 | Year 143 |
| 2.1-4 | Year 85,87,127,143 |
| 2.1-11 | New 35,36,45,50 |
| 2.5-27 | Year 87 |
| 2.43-47 | New 35 |
| 4.8-13 | Year 139 |
| 17.22-31 | Year 165 |

**Romans**

| | |
|---|---|
| 6.3-4 | Year 53 |
| 6.9-11 | Year 75; Sing 11,12 |
| 8.22 | Year 31 |
| 8.26 | Year 85 |
| 12.1-2 | New 43 |
| 12.2 | Year 163,165 |
| 12.4-5 | Year 69,85 |
| 15.29 | Year 53 |

**1 Corinthians**

| | |
|---|---|
| 3.19 | Year 97 |
| 5.7-8 | Year 75; Sing 11,12 |
| 11.23-25 | Year 67 |
| 12.12-13 | Year 85 |
| 12.12-27 | Year 69 |
| 13.13 | Year 97; New 50 |
| 15.20-22 | Year 75; Sing 11,12 |
| 15.55-56 | Year 31,119; Sing 35,36 |

**2 Corinthians**

| | |
|---|---|
| 3.17 | Year 87 |
| 5.17 | Year 77; Sing 25,26 |
| 12.9 | Year 25; Sing 15,16 |

**Galatians**

| | |
|---|---|
| 4.4 | Year 31; New 36 |
| 5.22-23 | Year 19 |
| 6.9 | New 21 |

**Ephesians**

| | |
|---|---|
| 4.1-6 | New 36 |
| 4.23 | Year 85 |
| 4.25 | Year 69 |

**Philippians**

| | |
|---|---|
| 2.5-11 | New 26,27,28 |

**Colossians**

| | |
|---|---|
| 3.1-2 | Year 19 |

**1 Timothy**

| | |
|---|---|
| 6.12 | Year 95 |

**Hebrews**

| | |
|---|---|
| 1.2 | Year 37 |
| 6:20-7.28 | Year 45 |
| 13.2 | Year 39 |

**1 Peter**

| | |
|---|---|
| 2.4-10 | Year 125; New 54 |
| 2.9 | Year 45 |
| 2.25 | Year 127 |
| 4.9 | Year 39 |
| 5.14 | Year 139 |

**1 John**

| | |
|---|---|
| 4.7-12 | Year 69 |
| 4.9 | Year 37 |

**3 John**

| | |
|---|---|
| 5-8 | Year 39 |

**Revelation**

| | |
|---|---|
| 4.8 | Year 119; Sing 35,36 |
| 4.11 | Year 115,119; Sing 29,30,35,36 |
| 5.5 | Year 17; Sing 3,4 |
| 5.6-14 | Year 19; New 54 |
| 5.9-10,13 | Year 115,119; Sing 29,30,35,36 |
| 5.10 | Year 125 |
| 5.11-12 | Year 129 |
| 7.9-17 | Year 119; Sing 35,36 |
| 12.14-19 | Year 13 |
| 15.3-417.14 | Year 23 |
| 19.6-9 | Year 15 |
| 19.16 | Year 23 |
| 21.2 | Year 127 |
| 21.21 | Year 15 |
| 22.16 | Year 23,37 |

# TOPICAL INDEX

Calvary
Year 155; New 23

Cana
Year 43; New 26,27

Eden
New 9,10,50

Egypt
Year 39; New 26,27

Emmaus
New 26,27

Galilee
Year 27,143; New 24

Jerusalem/Zion
Year 15,21,47,61,65,103,141,147;
Sing 21,22,31,32; New 3,16,23

Jordan River
Year 43,45,143

Nazareth
Year 27,155

Body of Christ
Year 67,69,81,85; New 40,47

Christian Life
Year 19,45,49,67,103,105,143,165; New 7,
17,21,23,28,32,33,34,36,37,38,40,41,42,43,
44,45,47,48,49,54,55

Christmas:
see Jesus Christ— Birth/ Incarnation

The Church
Year 45,67,81,85,101,119,125,127; Sing 35,
36; New 1,36,44,45,47,55

Communion: see Eucharist

Community
Year 59,67,69,85,87,93,153,155,157; New 7,
8,36,39,40,44,45,46,48,49

Covenant/Law
Year 17,25,43,49,55,59,103,133; Sing 3,4,
15,16,27,28; New 47

Creation
Year 21,23,55,57,71,91,93,105,107,109,111,
115,117,133,149,153,157,167; Sing 1,2,3,4,
5,6,13,14,23,24,27,28,29,30,33,34; New 1,2,
5,6,9,10,12,15,22,29,35,36,41,42,43,45,50,
51

Death and Funerals
Year 13,17,31,37,43,53,75,135,145,149,163;
Sing 3,4,11,12,17,18; New 1,5,6,7,25,28,29,
30, 41,42,45

Dedication
Year 27,125,129,133,163,165; New 21,22,
23,24,25,32,36,40,43,44,45,46,48,49,50,53,
54

Doubt
Year 39,59,79,91,97,139; New 21,24,30,46,
53,57

Eucharist
Year 13,15,23,31,67,75,81,101,161; Sing 11,
12; New 25,28,29,33,34,40,41,44, 45,47,53,
55

Evening
Year 121; Sing 19,20; New 2,37

Faith
Year 13,19,39,45,49,59,67,79,87,91,95,97,
137,139,147; Sing 31,32; New 1,4,11,14,21,
22,24,38,40,43,44,45,46,48,49,50,52,53,54,
57

Forgiveness
Year 43,55,57,67,93,101,127,133,161,153;
Sing 23,24,27,28; New 24,32,40,42

Gifts and Talents
Year 67,85,105,127,157; New 40,48,49,53

Grace
Year 31,39,49,53,55,77,87,91,93,95,97,101,
117,125,127,163,165,167; Sing 25,26,27,28,
33,34; New 11, 22,25,26,27,30,32,35,36,38,
41,42,43,44,45,47,48,49,50,53,54,55

Guidance
Year 39,45,59,67,77,127,135,165; Sing 25,
26; New 5,6,21,35,37,43

Healing
Year 21,43,55,57,85,93,101,127,133,153,
163; Sing 23,24,27,28; New 25,26,27,38,41,
46,53

Holy Spirit
Year 43,45,53,59,67,85,87,101,125,127,143,
161,165; New 33,34,35,36,39,40,41,43,45,
46,48,49,50,53,55,57

Hope
Year 13,17,19,23,43,55,59,61,87,93,95,97,
167; Sing 3,4,27,28; New 4,14,21,24,28,30,
35,36,38,40,42,44,45,47,50,53,54,57

Hospitality
Year 39,161; New 25,26,27,31,33,34,36,39

Image of God
Year 53,127,149,153,161,165; New 12,17,
26, 27,31,36,39,40,42

Jesus Christ

    Messiah/Christ
    Year 13,17,43,45,121,139,143; Sing 3,
    4, 19,20

    Birth/Incarnation
    Year 15,23,27,31,33,35,37,67,119,127,
    129,153,155; Sing 7,8,35,36; New 1,
    25,26,27,28,36,43,45,47

    Baptism
    Year 43,45

    Temptation
    Year 45; New 57

    Ministry and Teaching
    Year 43,45,101,127,143,163; New 17,
    18,19,20,21,24,25,26,27,31,33,34,39,
    43,46,53

    Transfiguration
    Year 43,49; New 18,19,20

    Triumphal Entry
    Year 65; New 50

    Last Supper
    Year 67; New 1,26,27

    Passion
    Year 35,43,65,67,69,71,75,81,115,119,
    127,139,143,153,155,165;Sing 7,8, 11,
    12,29,30,35,36; New 1,18,19,20,23,26,
    27,28,29,30,41,50,53, 54

    Resurrection
    Year 31,35,37,75,79,81,119,149,153;
    Sing 7,8,11,12,35,36; New 1, 18,19,20,
    23,26,27,28,29,30,45,54,55

    Ascension
    Year 35,119; Sing 7,8,35,36

    Continuing Presence
    Year 13,23,67,69,101,127,161;
    New 33, 34,40,41,55

    Sovereignty
    Year 15,21,23,35,65,81,119,127,139,
    167; Sing 7,8,35,36

    Second Coming
    Year 13,15,69,119,167; Sing 35,36;
    New 26,27

Justice
Year 13,19,25,125,167; Sing 15,16; New 14,
15,24,52

Language for God
Year 91,95,109; Sing 1,2

Lent
Year 53,55,57,59,61; Sing 23,24,27,28

Light
Year 15,23,37,43,47,49,71,91,101,121,133,
145,149; Sing 17,18,19,20,21,22; New 1,2,
25,28,29,33,34,35,37,41,42,45,57

Lord's Supper: see Eucharist

Love
Year 13,19,21,31,35,37,43,59,69,71,77,85,
87,97,101,105,107,117,125,127,129,135,
153,155,161,163,165,167; Sing 5,6,7,8,25,
26,33,34; New 1,2,4,7,9,10,11,13,14, 15,17,
21,24,25,28,29,31,32,35,36,39,40,41,42,43,
44, 46,47,48,49,50,53,54,55,56,57

Marriage
Year 43; New 8

Mercy: see Forgiveness,Grace

Ministry and Service
Year 45,67,69,81,101,105,115,125,127,
129,137,143,161,163,165; Sing 29,30;
New 21,25,28,30,33,34,36,40,41,43,45,
46,47,48,49,52,53,54,55

117

Music
Year 15,21,61,77,91,93,95,101,107,109,111,
119,121,133,135,141,147,149; Sing 1, 2,5,6,
13,14,19,20,25,26,31,32,35,36; New 1,3,7,
11,13,14,15,16,17,32,35,40,41,44,48,49,53

Offering
Year 67,105,129; New 28,43,51

Peace
Year 13,17,21,23,31,33,35,37,47,67,69,85,
87,93,153,161,167; Sing 3,4,7,8,21,22;
New 8,13,14,15,21,24,28,33,34,40,41,45,48,
49,52,53,55

Pentecost: see Holy Spirit

Pilgrimage
Year 19,39,45,53,59,61,77,103,129,137;
Sing 25,26; New 2,5,6,23,38,43,56

Prayer
Year 13,23,35,85,95,103,127,155; Sing 7,8;
New 17,28,37,38,40,44,45,48,49,52

Protection
Year 17,25,39,59,77,109,135,147; Sing
1,2,3, 4,15,16,25,26,31,32; New
2,4,11,22,37,41, 44,57

Repentance
Year 19,53,55,57,133; Sing 23,24,27,28;
New 12,32,40,41,42,47,53

Scripture
Year 13,23,133,161; New 21,33,34,40,44,55

Scripture Hymns (see Scripture Index)

Social Concerns
Year 81,125,153,155; New 11,14,17,18,19,
20,24,26,27,29,31,33,34,36,39,42,47,52,55

Thankfulness
Year 67,105,107,109,147,157; Sing 1,2,5,6,
31,32; New 1,13,14,15,16,17,51

Trinity
Year 35,53,87,113,119,127; Sing 7,8,9,10,
35,36; New 36,39,45,46,47,51

Unity
Year 67,69,85,93,107,127; Sing 5,6; New 7,
8,35,39,40,46,48,49

Worship
Year 15,17,35,49,61,67,95,97,101,103,105,
107,109,111,113,115,117,119,133,135,161;
Sing 1,2,3,4,5,6,7,8,9,10,13,14,29,30,33,34,
35,36; New 1,11,13,15,28,32,33,34,40,43,
44,45,51

# METRICAL INDEX

SM
Year 53

SMD
New 17,55

CM
Year 137,163; New 33,34

CM with refrain
Year 141

CMD
Year 17,47,59,71,95; Sing 3,4,21,22;
New 1, 14,15,48,49,50,54,56

CMD with refrain
New 36

LM
Year 33,113; Sing 9,10; New 8,51

LM with refrain
New 30

LMD
Year 133,167;New 32,47

65.65.D
Year 31

665.665.786
New 57

66.66.33.6
Year 153

66.66D
New 24

66.66.88
New 7

66.84.D
Year 109; Sing 1,2

67.67.66
New 31

69.669
New 5,6

76.76.D
Year 25,81,101; Sing 15,16; New 2

76.76.77.6
Year 37

76.86D with refrain
New 52

76.86.86
New 22,25

77.77
Year 23; New 35,42

77.77.77
Year 91; New 38

7777.77
Year 35; Sing 7,8

77.77.D
Year 19,43,55,87; Sing 27,28; New 37,46

84.84.888.4
New 41

86.86.44.6
Year 135

86.86.86
Year 79,103,117; Sing 33,34

86.86.87.86.86.86
Year 157

87.87
Year 57; Sing 23,24; New 44

87.87.6
Year 85

87.87.77.88
New 43

87.87.87
Year 67

87.87.87 with refrain
New 18,19,20

87.87.D
    Year 13,39,49,93,105,127,129,143,147,
    161,165; Sing 31,32; New 26,27,45

87.87.887
    Year 111; Sing 13,14

88.88.88
    Year 139

89.8.89.8.66.4.88
    Year 15

96.99.96
    Year 65

97.98.98.98
    Year 21

98.98
    Year 121; Sing 19,20

98.98 with refrain
    New 12

98.98.88
    New 53

98.98.D
    Year 45; New 16

9 12.10 10.12 12.4
    New 40

10.10.10 with alleluia(s)
    Year 75; Sing 11,12

10.10.10.5
    New 13

10.10.10.10
    Year 61,97,125; New 11,39

10.10.10.10.10
    Year 107; Sing 5,6

10 10.10 10.10 10
    Year 145; Sing 17,18; New 4

10.10.11.11
    New 9,10,29

11 10.11 10
    Year 149; New 21,28

11.11.11.5
    Year 115,119; Sing 29,30,35,36; New 23

12.10.12.10
    Year 155

12.12.12.12 with refrain
    Year 69

14.14.478
    Year 77; Sing 25,26

Irregular
    New 3

Irregular with refrain
    Year 27

# AN ALPHABETICAL LIST OF TUNES
## in *To Sing God's Praise* and
## *New Psalms and Hymns and Spiritual Songs*

ACCORD
New 48
ALDINE
New 22
ALEXANDRA
New 1
AR HYD Y NOS
New 41
ARISE
Sing 23
BENTBROOK
Sing 34
BICKFORD
New 23
BINGHAM
New 35
BY THE WATERS
New 3
CAELITES PLAUDANT
Sing 35
CANTICUM NOVUM
New 15
CASADAY
New 56
COMPLAINER
New 2
COSTLY GIFTS
New 43
COVENANT
New 47
DANCE OF GRACE
Sing 28
DARNEL
New 24
DAVID EARLE
New 31
DECATUR PLACE
Sing 36
DINBYCH
New 55
DIX
Sing 7
DOWNING
New 34
EAGLEVILLE
Sing 6
ECCE, DEUS
Sing 32
EMMANUEL PARISH, WESTON
New 40

EMMAUS
Sing 24
ENDLESS FEAST
New 25
ENGELBERG
Sing 11
FOREST GREEN
New 50
HACKETT
New 20
HAMMERLING
Sing 12
HOLY PEOPLE
New 36
HOLY TRINITY, THE AMERICAN
CATHEDRAL
New 18
IMAGO DEI CAZENOVIA
New 12
IMMACULATA
New 6
IN BABILONE
Sing 31
JACOB
Sing 10
JESU, MEINE FREUDE
New 57
JULION
New 38
KINGSFOLD
Sing 3; New 54
LEONI
Sing 1
LOBE DEN HERREN
Sing 25
LOMBARD STREET
New 21
LONG ISLAND SOUND
New 10
LOOSE CANON
New 13
LUX TREMENDA
New 19
MADDEN
Sing 30
MARVIL
New 30
MERCER STREET
New 17

# COMPOSER AND ARRANGER INDEX

| | |
|---|---|
| Sheets, Dorothy Howell (b. 1915) | Sing 4; New 35 |
| Simms, Linda Hoffer (b. 1950) | New 47 |
| *Southern Harmony*, 1835 | Sing 2; New 2 |
| Stanford, Charles Villiers (1852-1924) | Sing 11; New 44 |
| Tallis, Thomas (1505?-1585) | Sing 21,32 |
| Teschner, Melchior (1584-1635) | Sing 15 |
| Traditional | New 3 |
| Traditional American | New 16 |
| Traditional Dutch | Sing 31 |
| Traditional English | Sing 3; New 8,50,54 |
| Traditional Irish | New 44 |
| Traditional Welsh | New 41 |
| Vaughan Williams, Ralph (1872-1958) | Sing 3,17,35; New 4,50,54 |
| *Vesperale*, 1746 | Sing 29 |
| West, Martin (b. 1929) | New 8 |
| White, David Ashley (b. 1944) | Sing 12,18,20; New 5,18 |
| *Whole Booke of Psalmes*, 1621 | New 9 |
| Willan, Healey (1880-1968) | Sing 29 |
| Williamson, Malcolm (b. 1931) | Sing 8; New 17 |
| Wilson, John (1905-1992) | Sing 21 |
| Woodman, James (b. 1957) | Sing 22,30,30 |
| Young, Carlton R. (b. 1926) | New 37 |

# INDEX OF FIRST LINES